I ♥ ORIGAMI

Buster Books

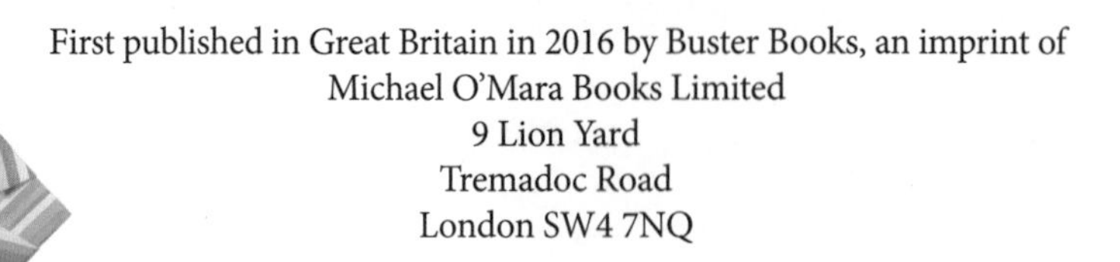

First published in Great Britain in 2016 by Buster Books, an imprint of
Michael O'Mara Books Limited
9 Lion Yard
Tremadoc Road
London SW4 7NQ

A CIP catalogue record for this book is available from the British Library.

Papers used by Michael O'Mara Books Limited are natural, recyclable products made from wood grown in sustainable forests. The manufacturing processes conform to the environmental regulations of the country of origin.

ISBN: 978-1-78055-451-8 in paperback print format

1 3 5 7 9 10 8 6 4 2

Designed and typeset by Claire Cater
Cover and interior photographs and diagrams by David Woodroffe

Printed and bound in China

 www.busterbooks.co.uk  Buster Children's Books  @BusterBooks

FOUR MODELS IN THIS BOOK REFER TO INSIDE REVERSE FOLDS AND THE FOLLOWING DIAGRAMS SHOW HOW TO DO THEM:

1.

Note from the diagram where the fold needs to be.

2.

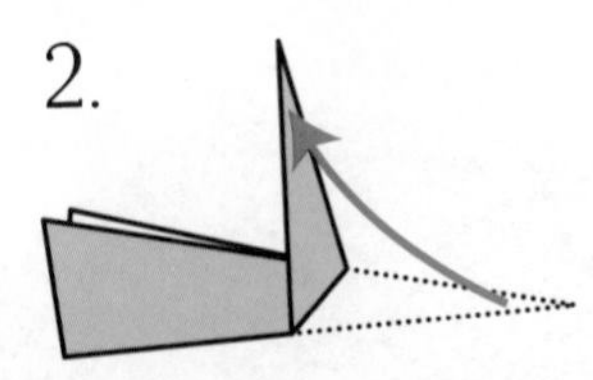

Fold the flap towards you and in front of the rest of the part. Crease and unfold.

3.

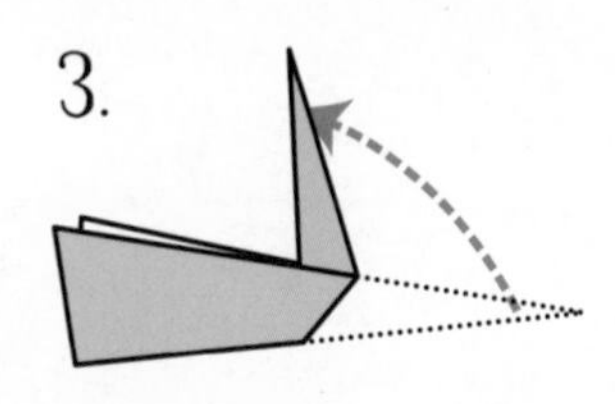

Now fold the flap again along the same crease, but this time away from you and behind. Crease and unfold.

4.

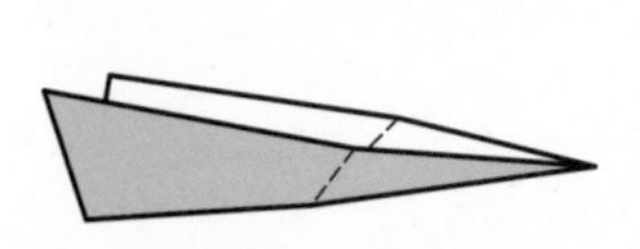

Pull apart the two sides of the flap.

5.

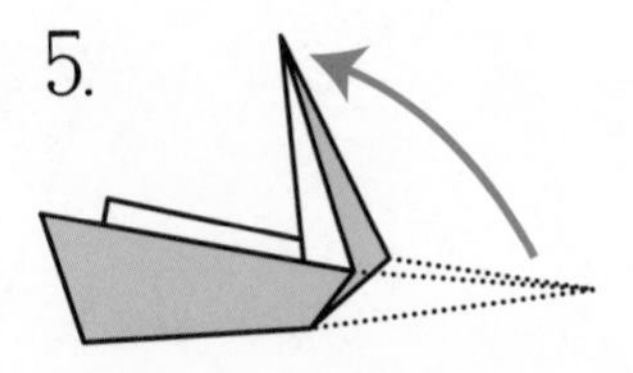

Push the point of the flap inside the gap you have just made.

6.

Flatten and crease.

BIRD

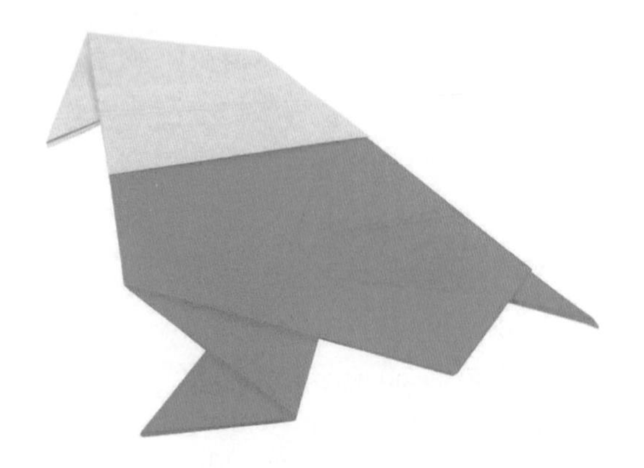

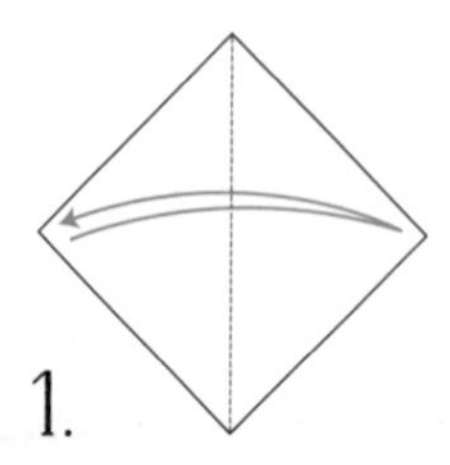

1.

Place your square with the white side up. Fold the left corner across to the right one, then crease and unfold.

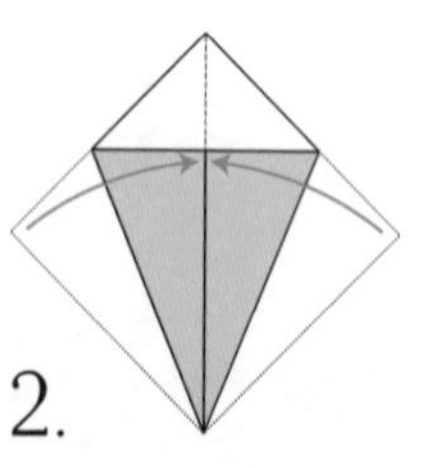

2.

Fold the lower left-hand edge to the centre crease, and fold. Repeat with the right-hand lower edge.

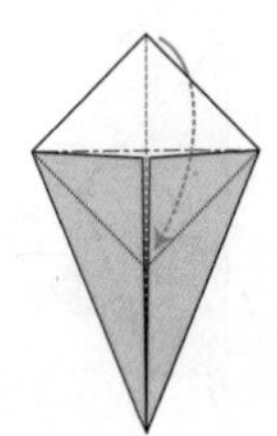

3.

Now fold the top corner down behind the model and crease along a line that lies between the left and right points.

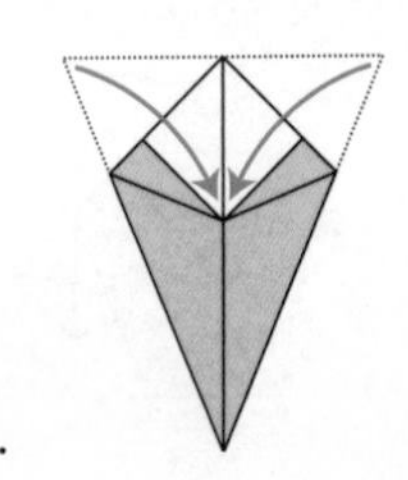

4.

Fold the top left-hand corner down at 45° to the centre and then repeat with the right-hand top point.

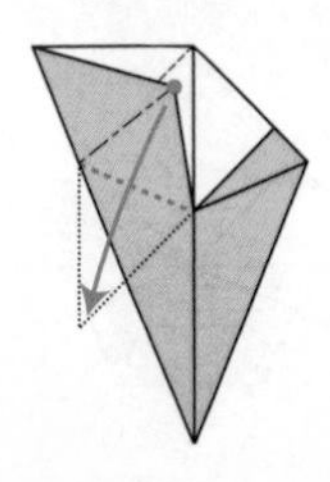

5.

Unfold the left-hand fold that you did in step 4. Take the front left-hand centre point, shown by the red dot, pull down and crease well along the heavy dotted line as shown.

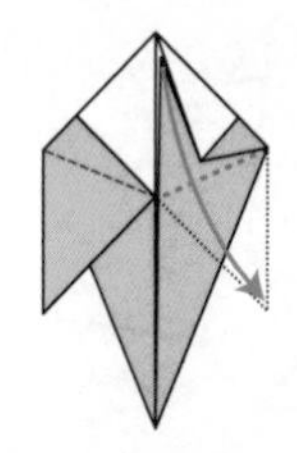

6.

Repeat step 5 with the right-hand side.

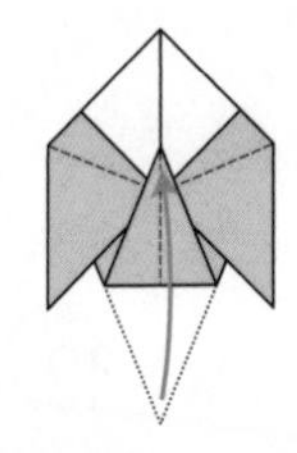

7.

Fold the tail up and crease well as shown.

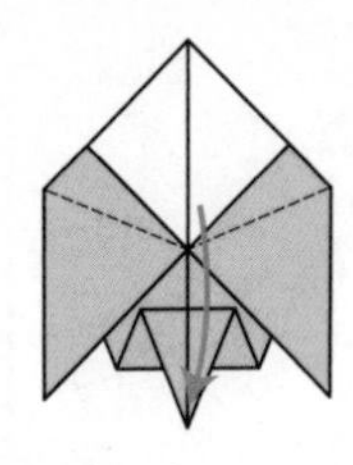

8.

Fold the tip down and crease well at the position show

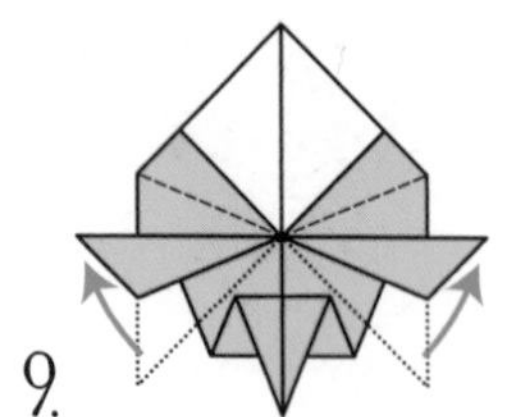

Fold up and crease the two lower side points.

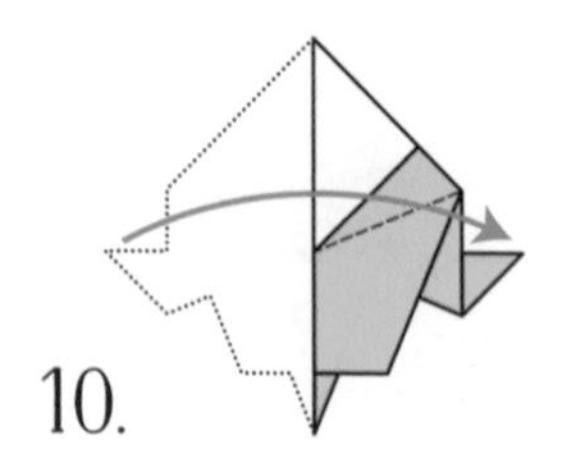

Fold the model in half by bringing the left side over the right. Crease well.

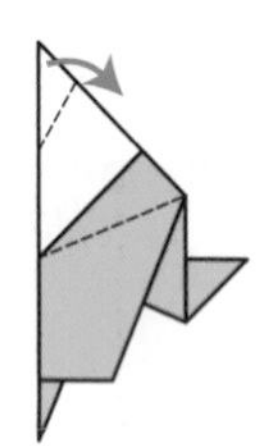

Fold forward and crease the top point along the dotted line shown, then open and fold back. Crease and unfold.

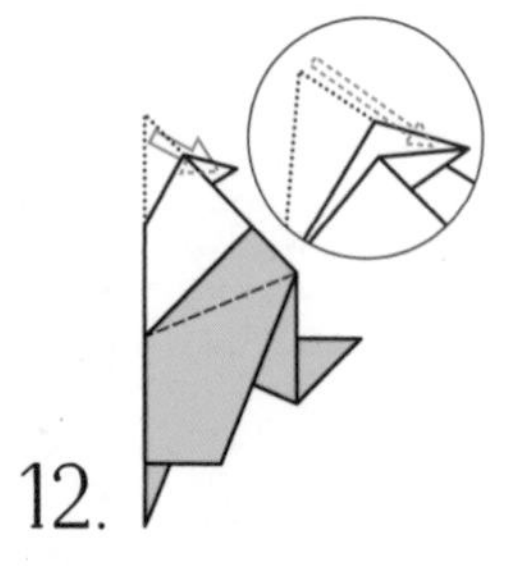

Inside reverse fold on the line you've just made in step 11 (see the inset diagram).

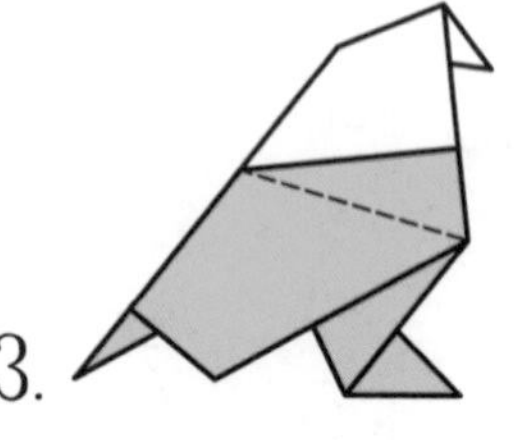

Your finished bird should now look like this.

TURTLE

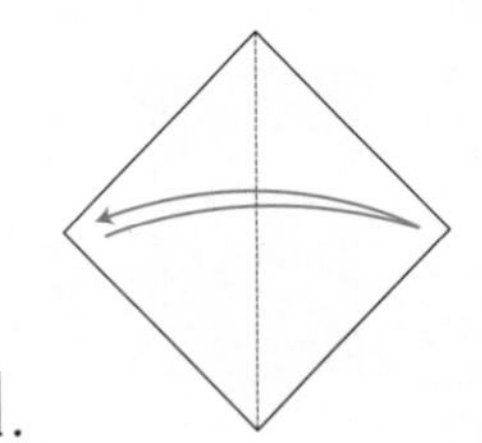

1.

With the white side up, fold the left corner over to the right, crease and unfold.

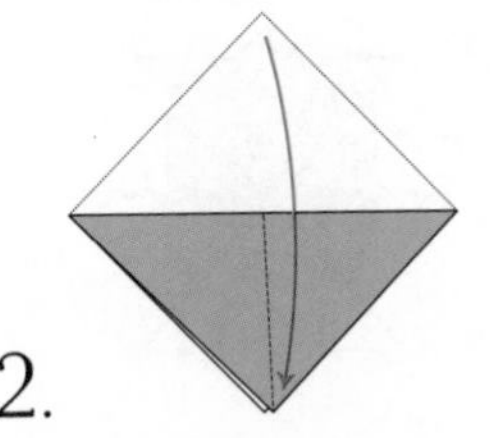

2.

Bring the top point down to the bottom one and crease.

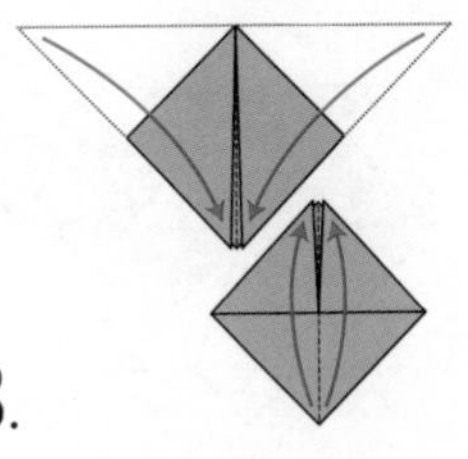

3.

Fold the left and right points down 45° to the bottom point. Then fold the two front points at the bottom up to the top point. Crease well.

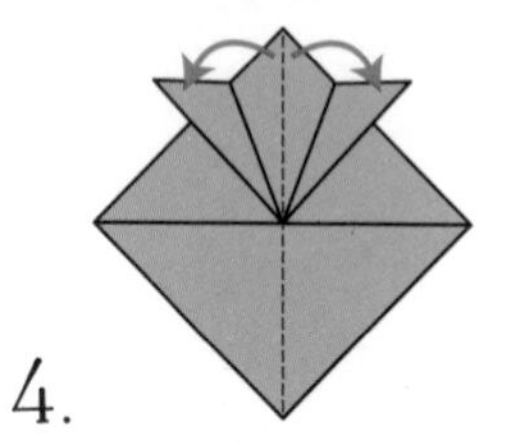

4.

Fold the two top points outwards as shown.

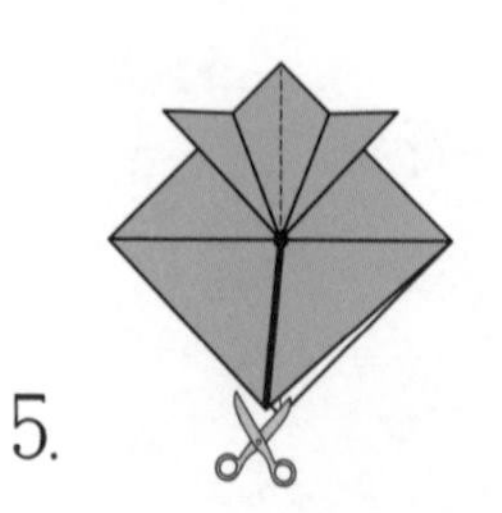

5.

On the top layer only, cut along the crease from the bottom point up to the middle.

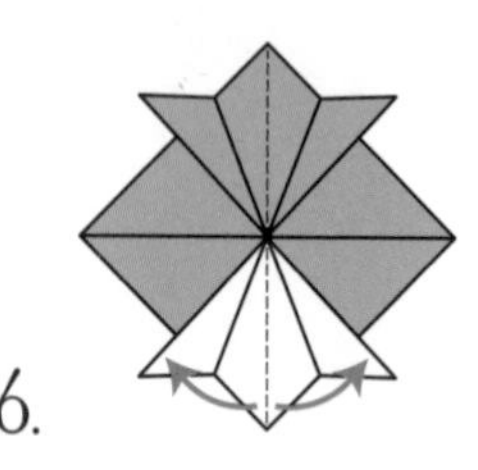

6.

Fold out the two bottom points as shown.

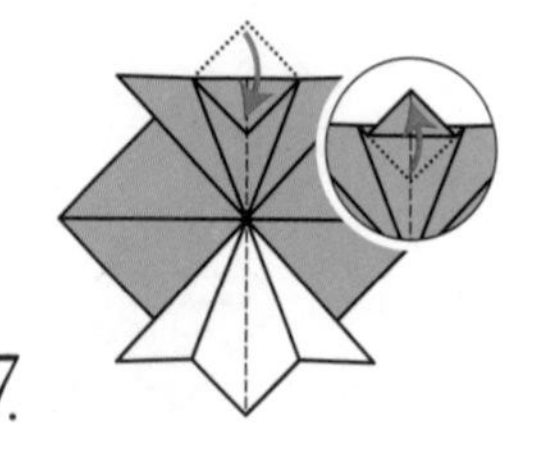

7.

Fold down the top point along the line level with the two top flaps. Then fold it up along a line just below the first crease.

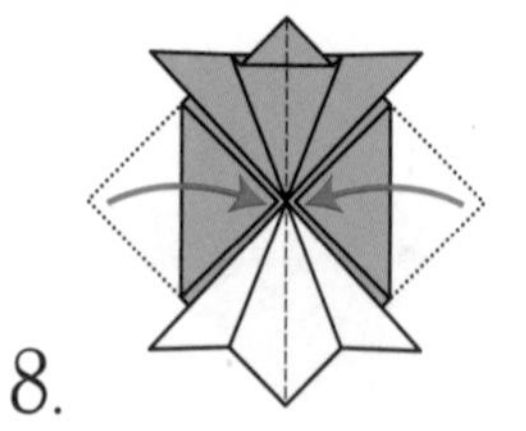

8.

Fold the left and right points almost to the centre and crease well.

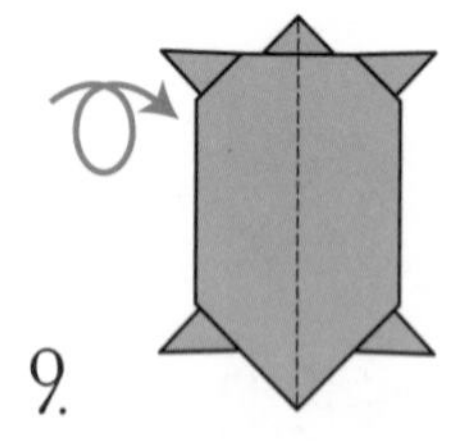

9.

Flip your finished turtle the right way up.

BUTTERFLY

1. 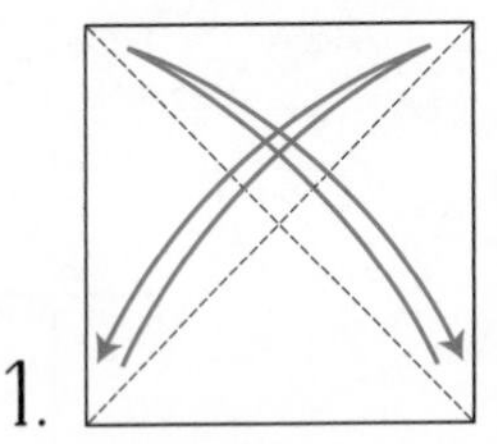

Take a square, white side up. Fold the bottom left corner up to the top right. Crease and unfold. Then repeat by folding the bottom right corner up to the top left and unfold.

2. 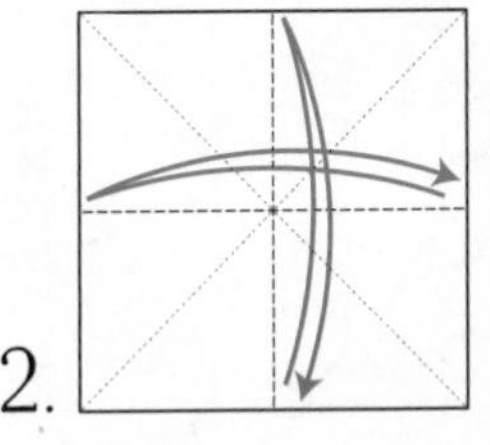

Fold the bottom edge up to the top one, crease and unfold. Then repeat by folding the right edge over to the left one. Crease and unfold.

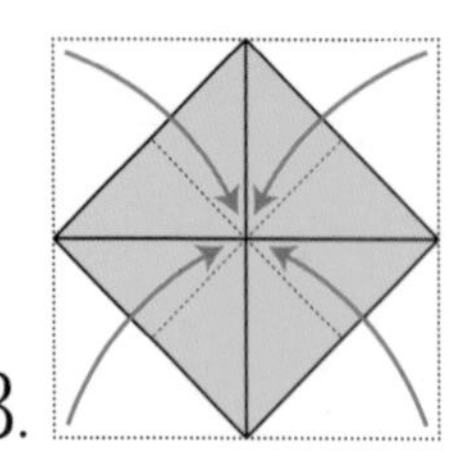

3\. Fold the four corners into the centre and crease the four sides.

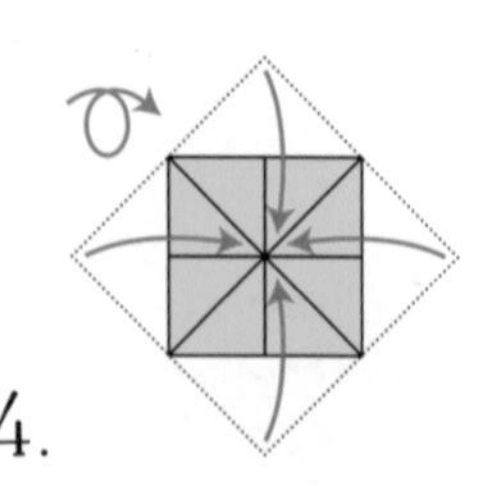

4\. Turn the model over and fold the four corners into the centre and crease the four sides.

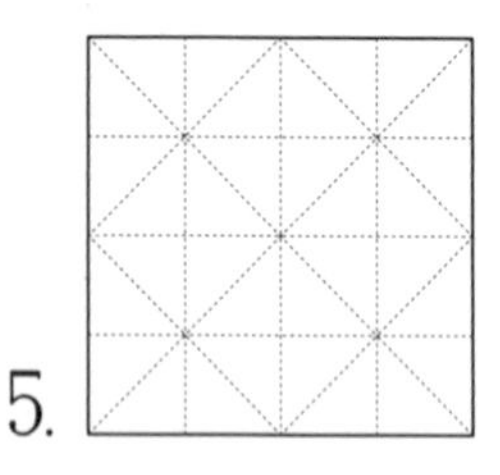

5\. Unfold the whole sheet and place with the white side up.

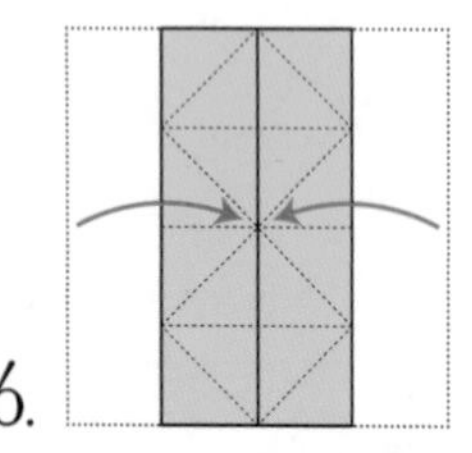

6\. Fold both side edges into the centre and crease the sides.

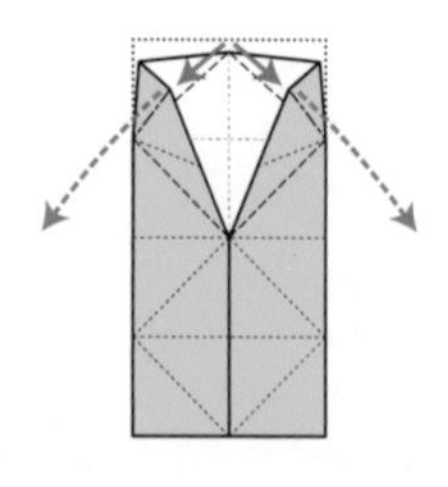

7\. Take the two top centre points and, one at a time, pull them out in the direction of the arrows.

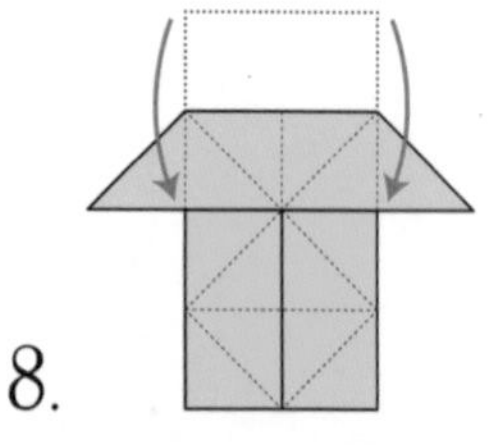

8\. When they are fully extended to the sides, flatten and crease the shape.

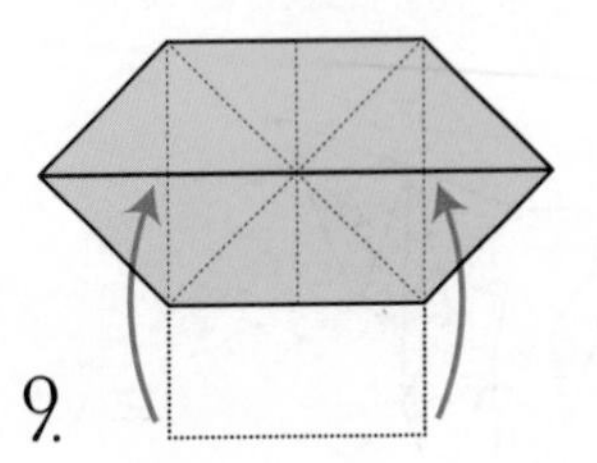

9.

Repeat steps 7 and 8 on the bottom half of the model.

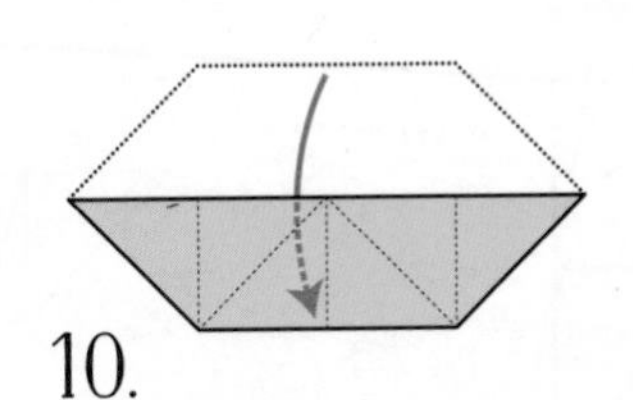

10.

Fold the top half back behind the bottom half and crease.

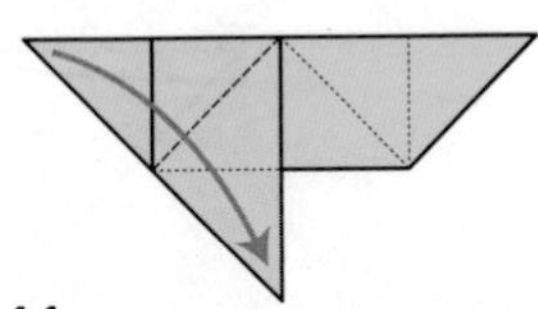

11.

Take the front left top point and fold it down as shown here.

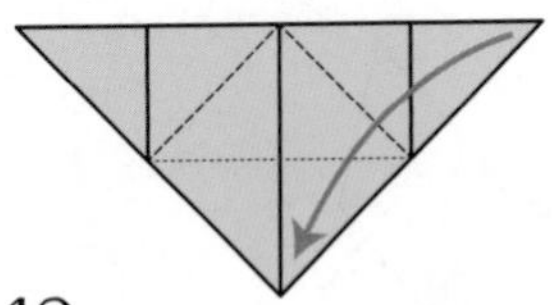

12.

Repeat step 11 with the right side.

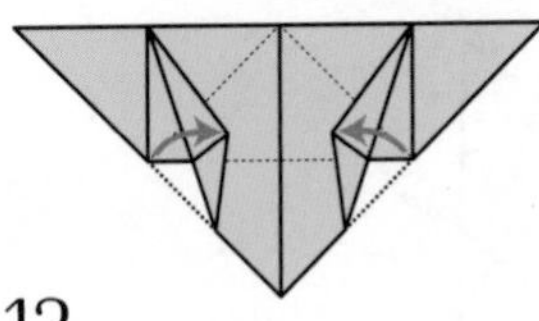

13.

Fold the two midpoints inwards as shown here and crease well.

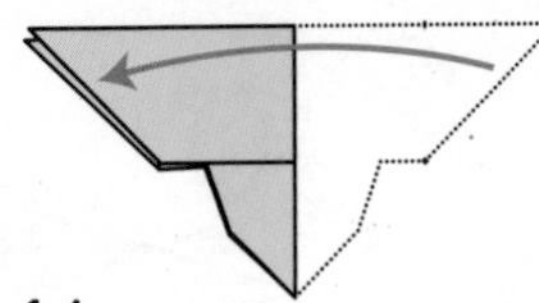

14.

Fold in half by taking the right side over to the left. Crease well.

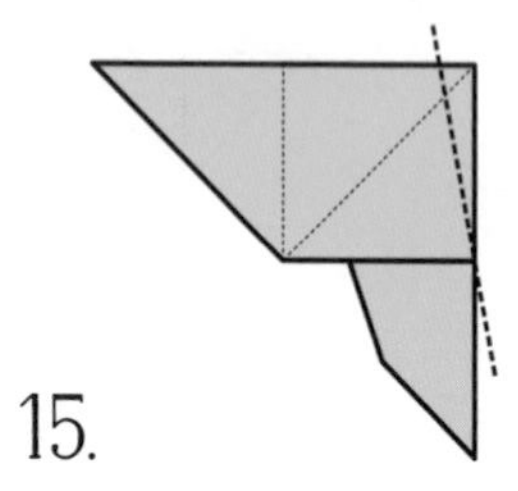

15.

Fold along the dashed line indicated. Crease and unfold. Fold the other way on the same line. Crease and unfold.

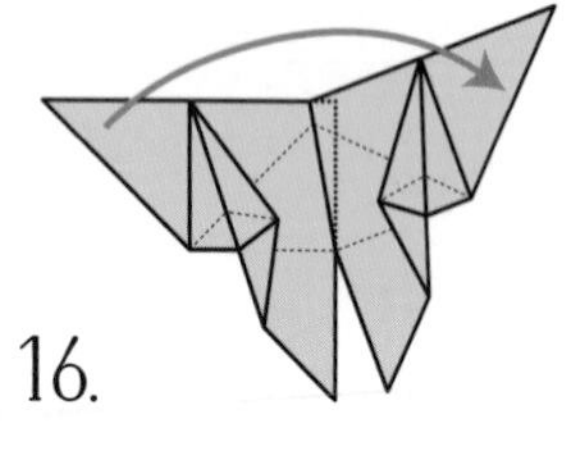

16.

Open the model.

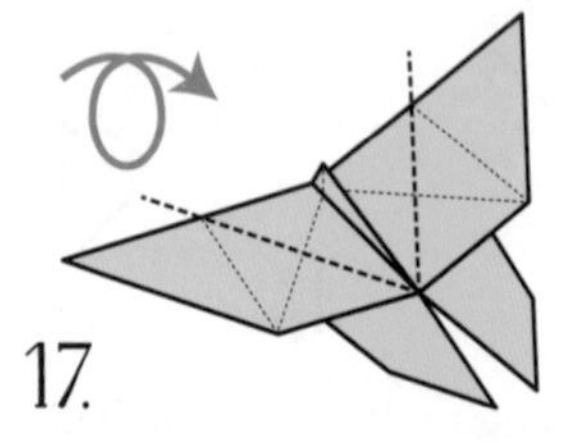

17.

Turn the butterfly over and fold the wings down along the dashed lines.

18.

Shape the model as shown.

FISH

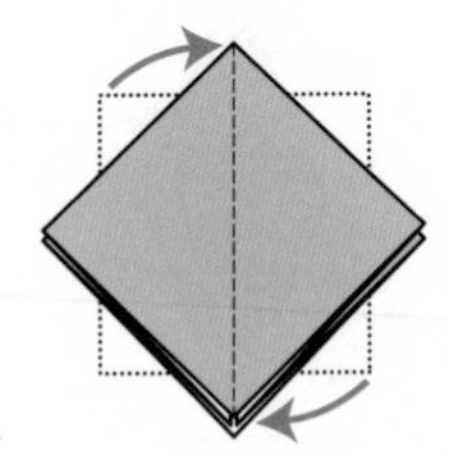

1.

To begin making this model follow steps 1 to 9 from the 'Star box' instructions and then turn the model 45° clockwise with the four points at the bottom.

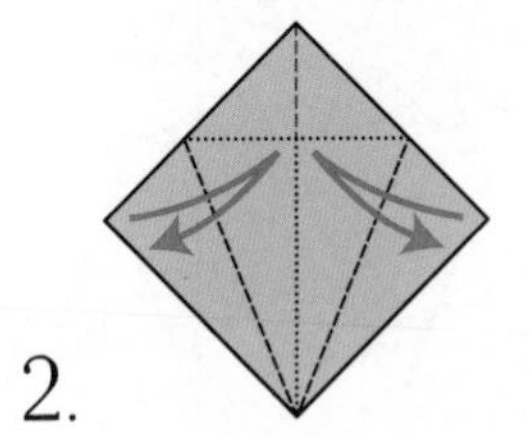

2.

Fold the front bottom left edge across to the centre line, crease and unfold. Then repeat with the front bottom right edge.

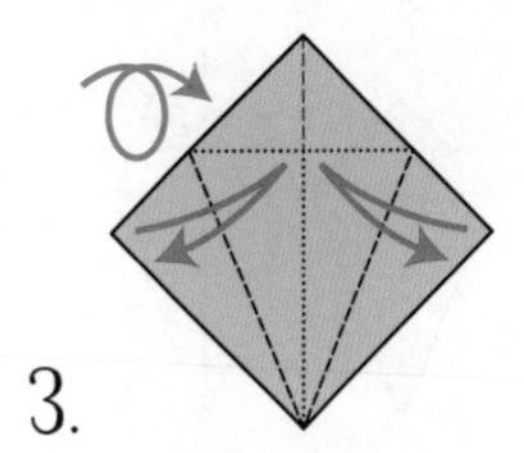

3.

Flip the model over and repeat the instructions in step 2.

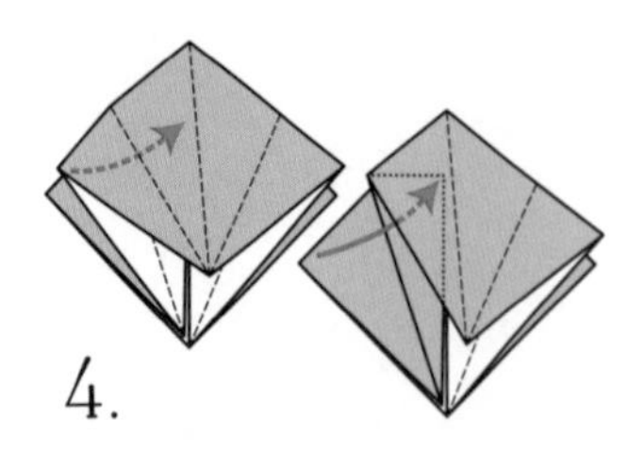

4.

Lift the bottom front corner, then push and reverse fold the left corner inside itself. Flatten and crease.

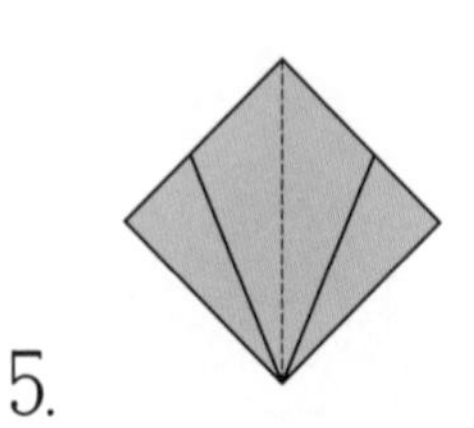

5.

Repeat step 4 with the right side of the model. It should now look like this.

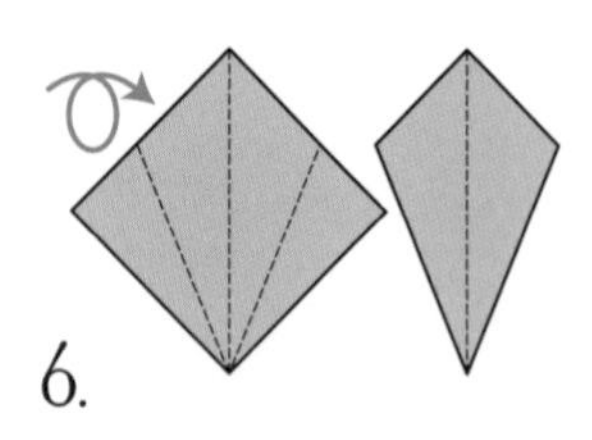

6.

Flip the model over and repeat steps 4 and 5 on this side.

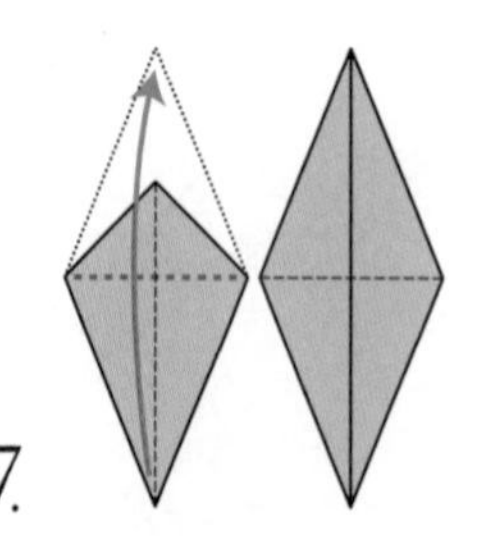

7.

Take the front bottom point, fold it up over the line shown by the red dotted line and crease.

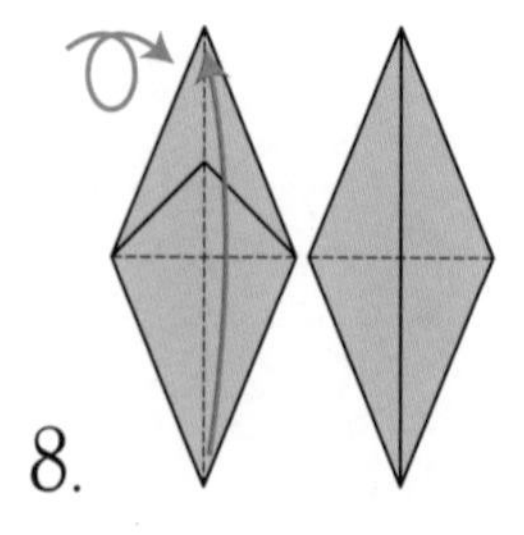

8.

Flip the model over and repeat step 7 on this side.

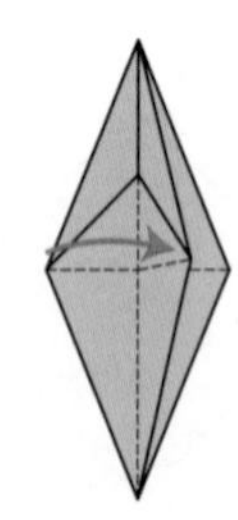

9.

Fold the left front half of the model over to the right and crease.

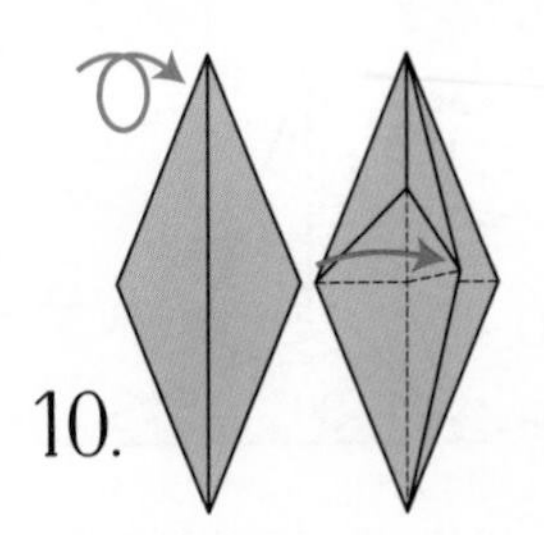

Flip the model over and fold the top left front half over to the right and crease.

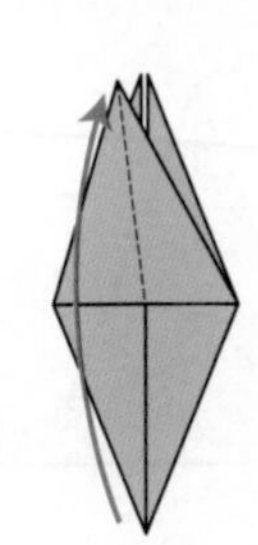

Take the front bottom point, fold it up and crease.

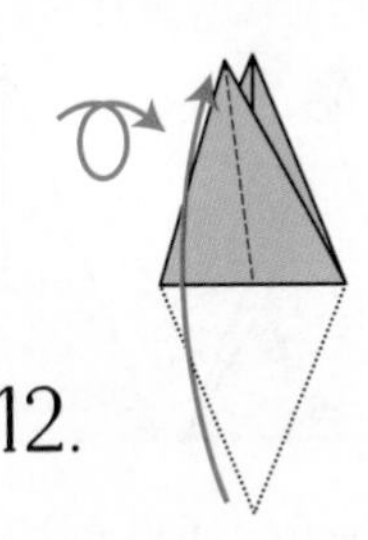

Flip the model over and fold the bottom point up to the top and crease.

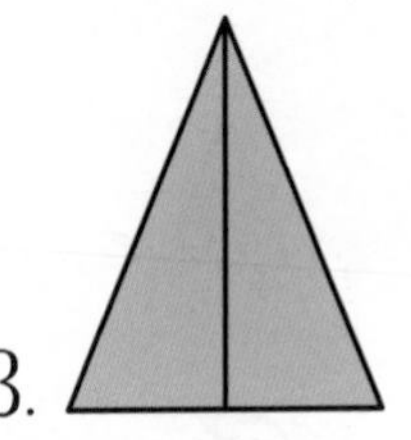

Your model should now look like this.

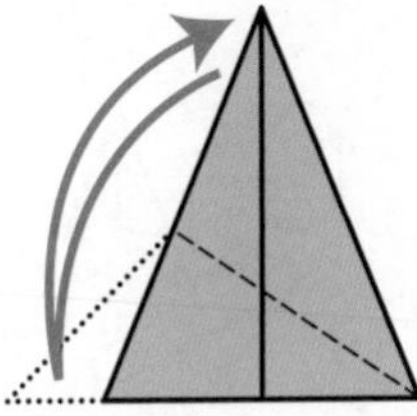
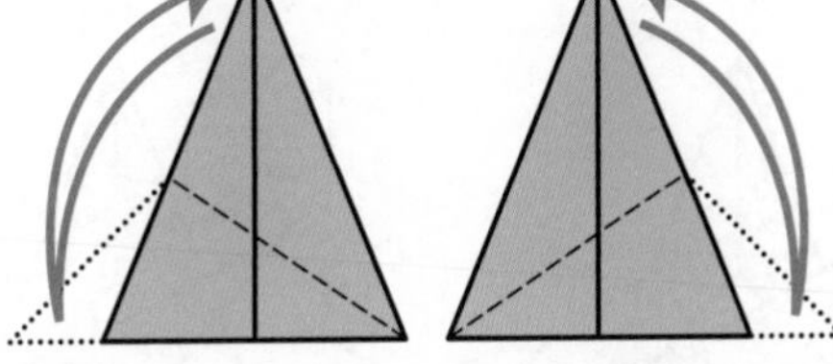

Fold the front top point down diagonally to the left so the right edge lines up with the bottom edge. Crease and unfold. Fold the front top point down to the right until its left edge lines up with the bottom edge. Crease and unfold. Flip the model over and repeat this step with the other side.

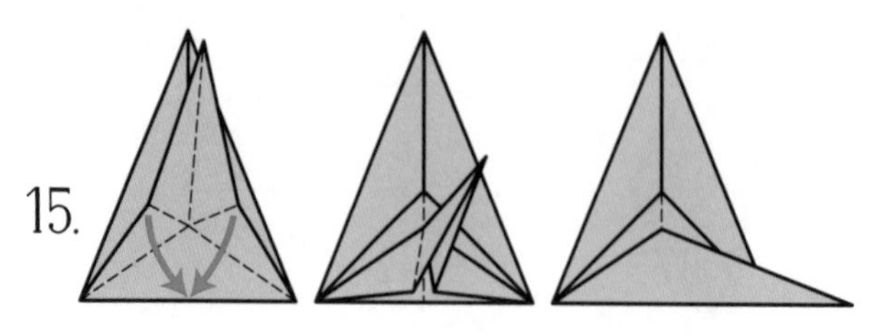

Take the front flap and fold it down towards you, at the same time pushing the sides inwards to create a forward-pointing flap, which you then fold to the right and crease.

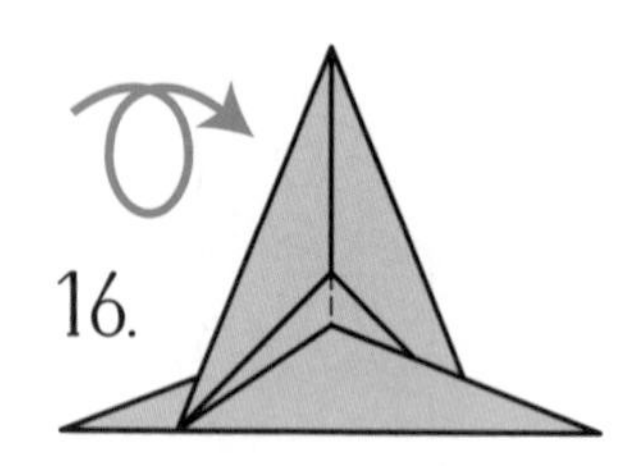

Flip the model over and repeat step 15 on this side.

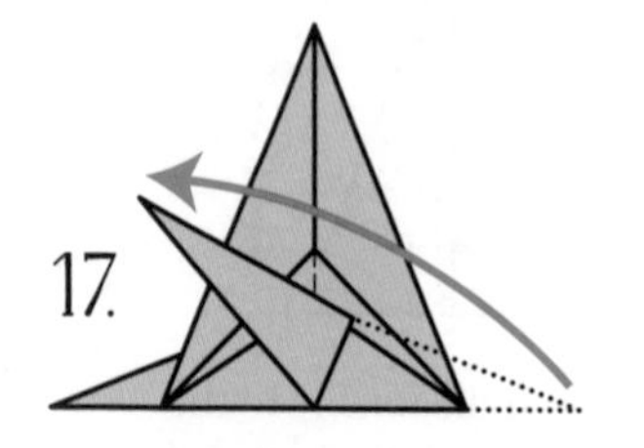

Fold the new flap across to the left at an angle as shown and crease.

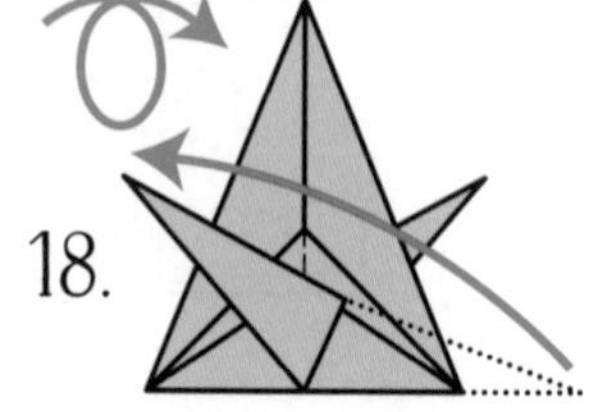

Flip the model over and repeat step 17 on this side.

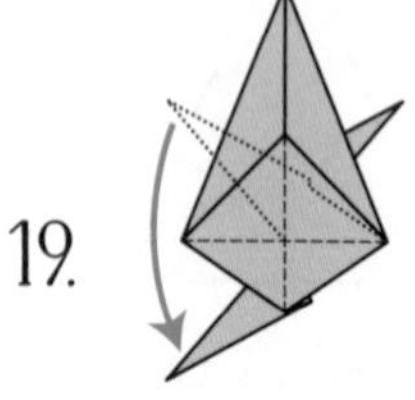

Fold the front flap down.

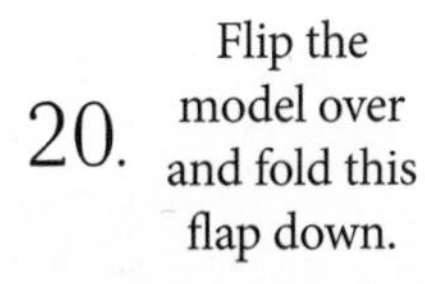

20. Flip the model over and fold this flap down.

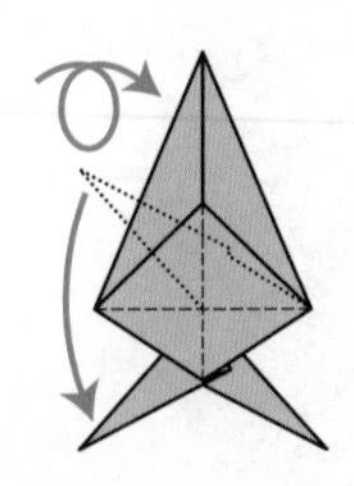

21. Turn the model 90° clockwise.

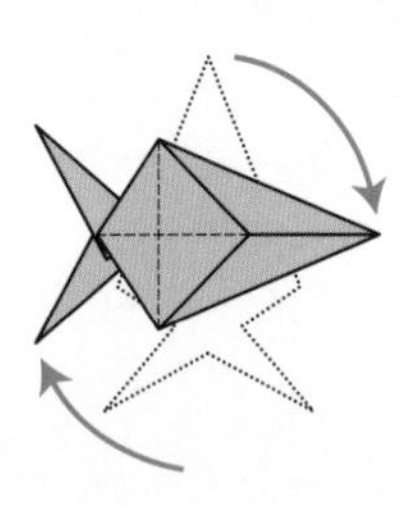

22. Open out the top right flap and inside reverse fold it so that the folded edge is level with the top point of the body, as in the diagram.

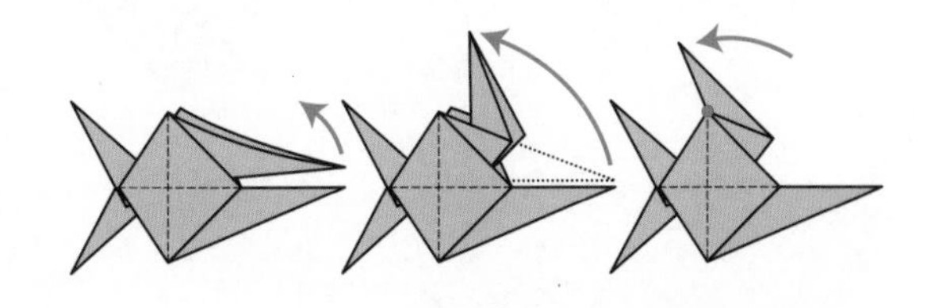

23.

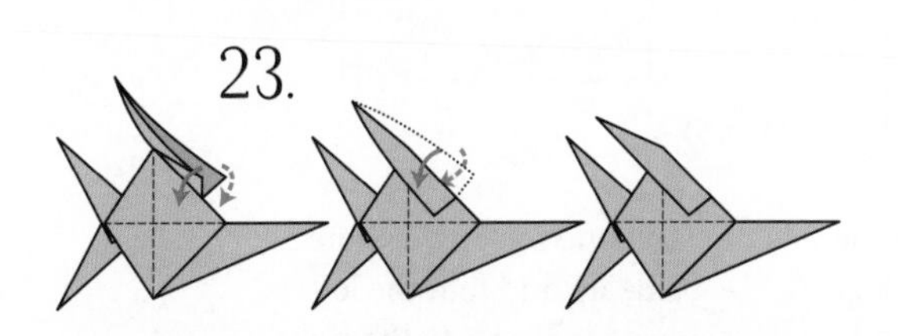

Fold apart the two front edges of the fin and back over the sides of the body then fold and crease flat.

24.

Repeat steps 22 and 23 with the lower right flap. Your model is now finished and should look like this.

HEART

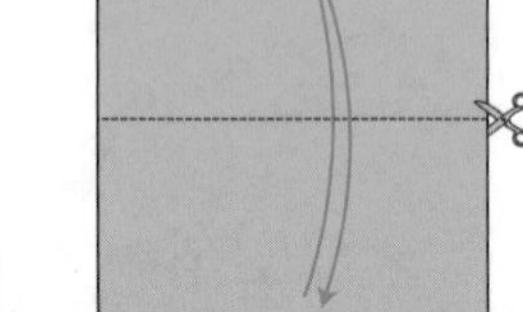

1.

Take a square and fold the bottom edge up to the top edge. Crease and unfold. Carefully cut along the crease to make two rectangles.

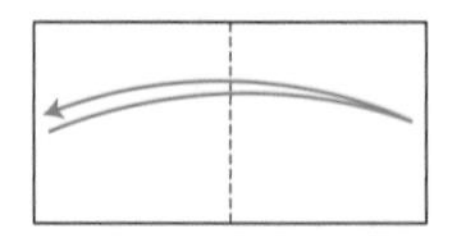

2.

Lay one rectangle white side up and fold the left side edge across to the right edge. Crease and unfold.

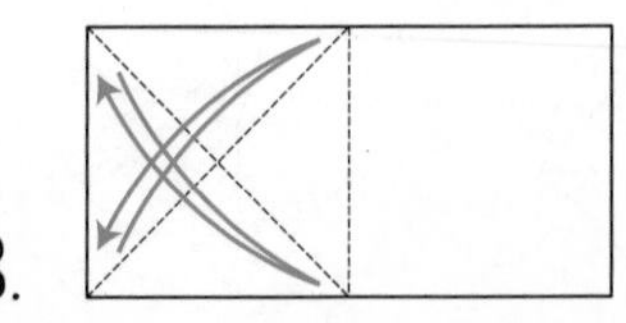

Fold the top left corner diagonally down to where the central crease meets the bottom edge. Crease and unfold. Now fold the bottom left corner diagonally up to where the central crease meets the top edge. Crease and unfold.

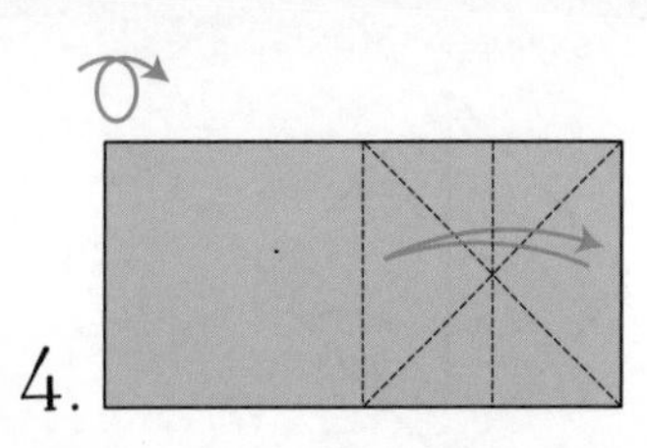

Flip the paper over and fold the right side edge over to the central crease. Crease and unfold.

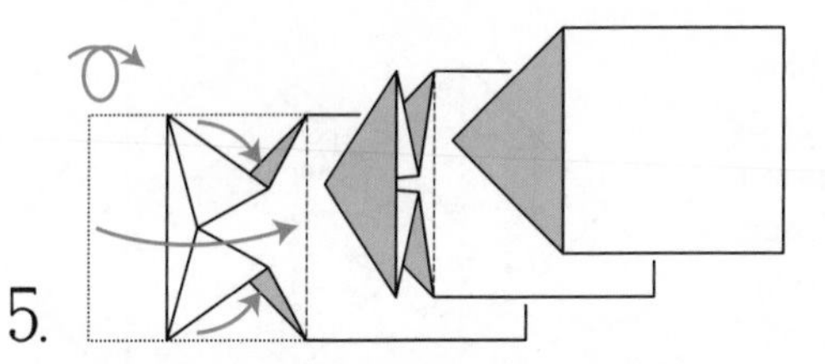

Flip the paper back to white side up. Fold over the left edge to the centre, pushing the sides in as shown in the three diagrams. Flatten the finished part well.

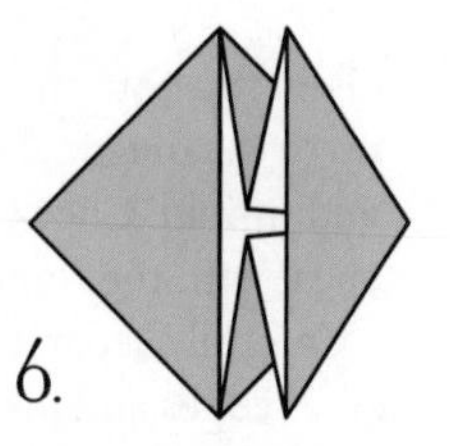

Repeat steps 3, 4 and 5 with the right half of the sheet.

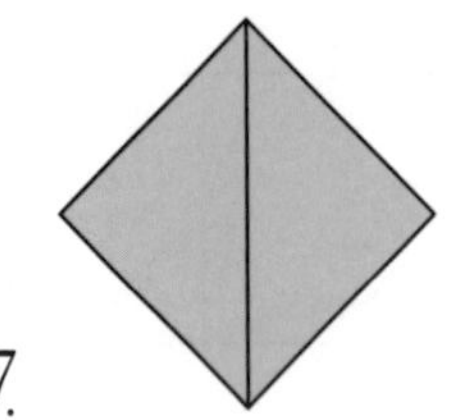

7.

Your model should now look like this.

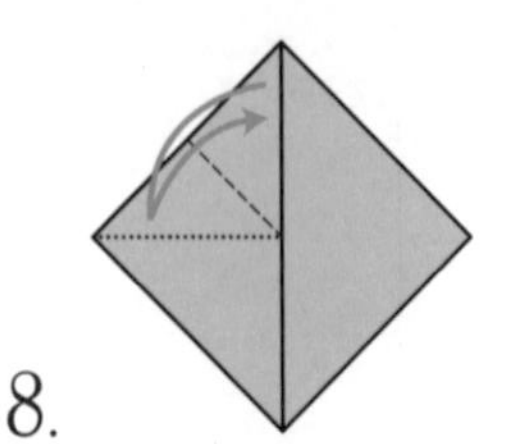

8.

Take the front left point at the top and fold it diagonally down to the point at the left side. Crease and unfold.

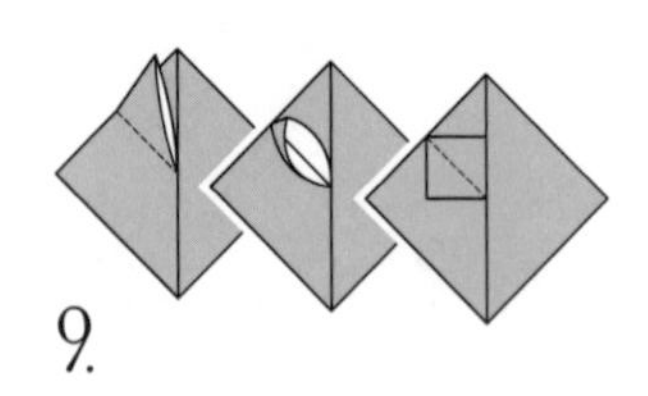

9.

Hold the new flap up and carefully open out the inner edge. Press down the outer edge and flatten to create a square.

10.

Fold the bottom edge of the square up to the diagonal centre line. Crease and unfold. Check with the diagram. Repeat with the right edge of the square. Carefully separate each of the two outer edges and press and flatten each one down to create two kite shapes.

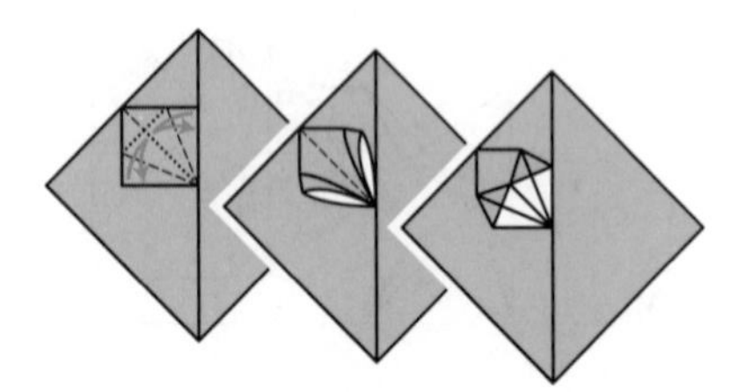

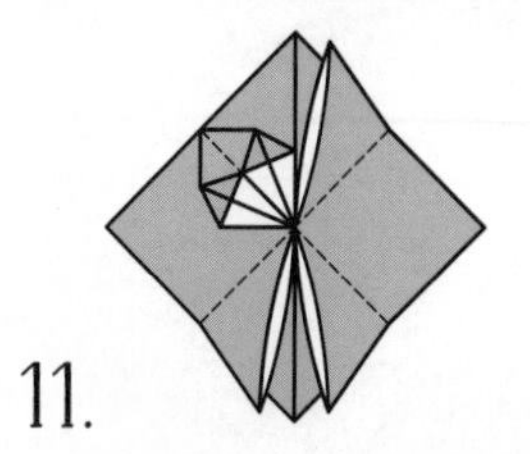

11.

Repeat steps 8, 9 and 10 with the remaining top front point and the bottom two front points.

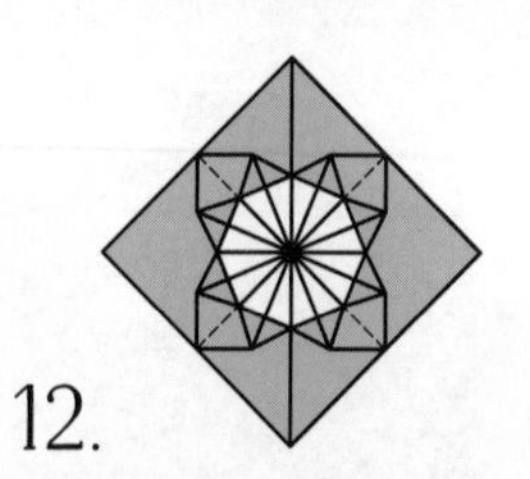

12.

Your heart should now look like this.

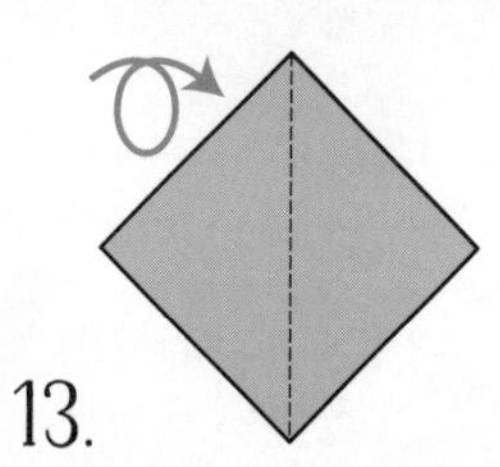

13.

Flip the model over.

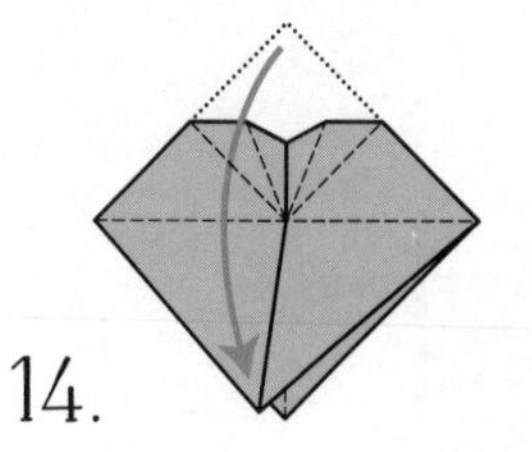

14.

Fold the top point down to the bottom and crease.

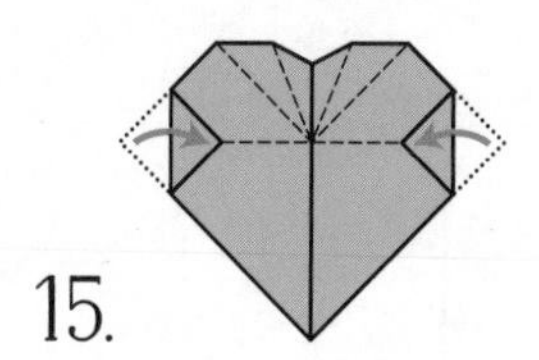

15.

Fold in the two outer points as shown and crease well.

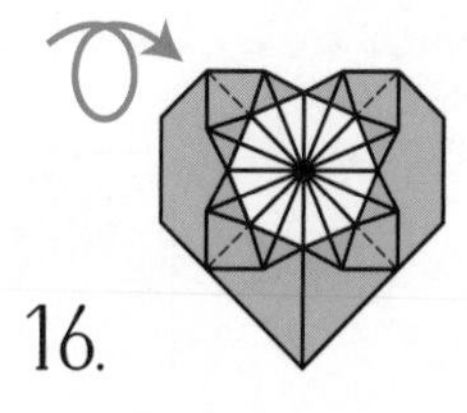

16.

Flip the model over to reveal your finished heart.

JUMPING FROG

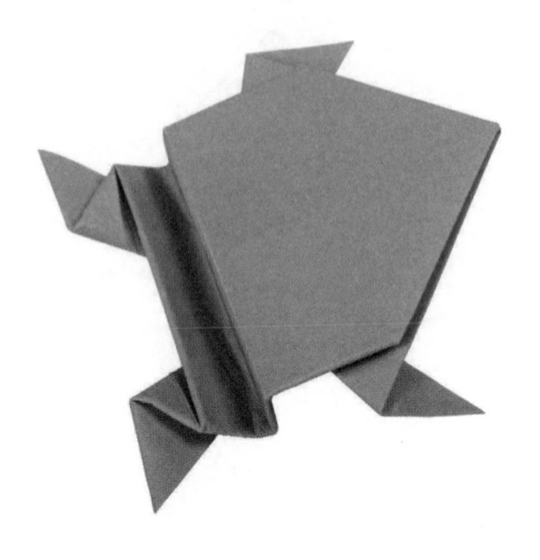

1.

Fold the bottom edge up to the top one. Crease and unfold.

2.

Fold the left edge over to the right and crease.

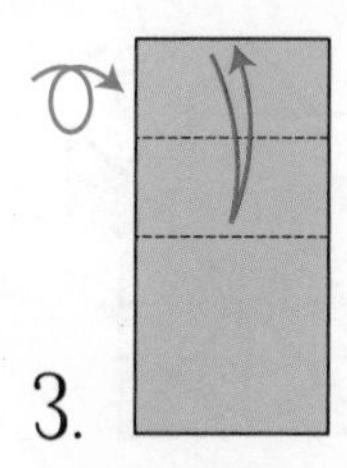

3.

Flip the model over and fold the top edge down to the centre fold. Crease and unfold.

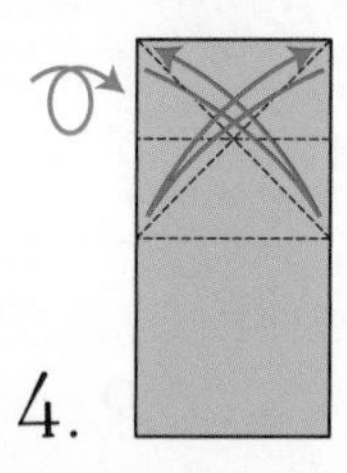

4.

Flip the model back and fold the top left corner diagonally down to the right edge of the centre fold. Crease and unfold. Repeat with the top right corner down and across to the left edge of the centre fold. Crease and unfold.

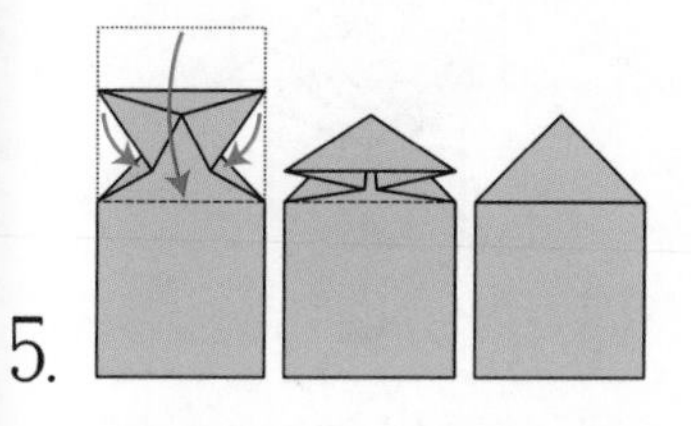

5.

Fold down the top edge to the centre, pushing the sides in as shown in the three diagrams. Crease the finished part well.

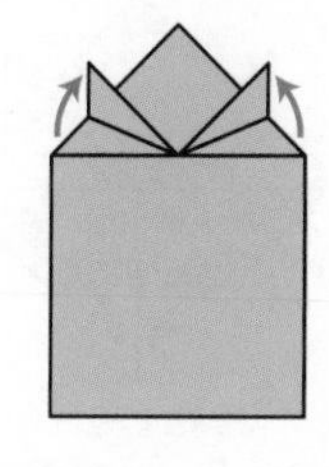

6.

Fold up the front legs at the angle shown.

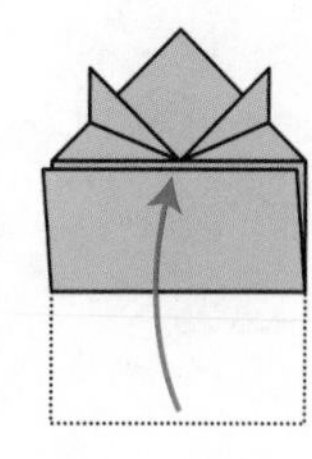

7.

Take the bottom edge and fold it up to the lower edge of the top triangle.

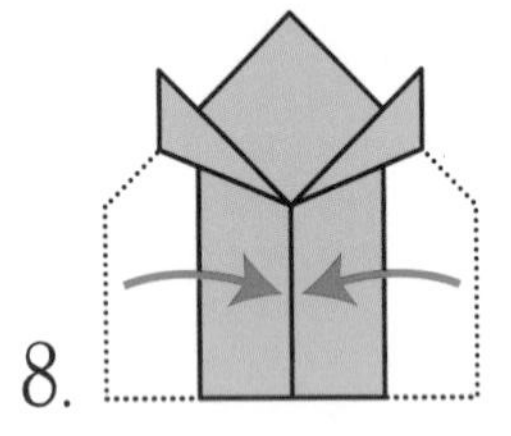

8.

Fold in the two side edges to the centre of the model, folding them under the top part.

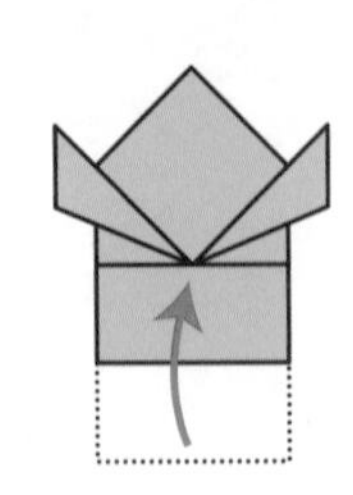

9.

Fold up the new bottom edge to the lower edge of the top triangle.

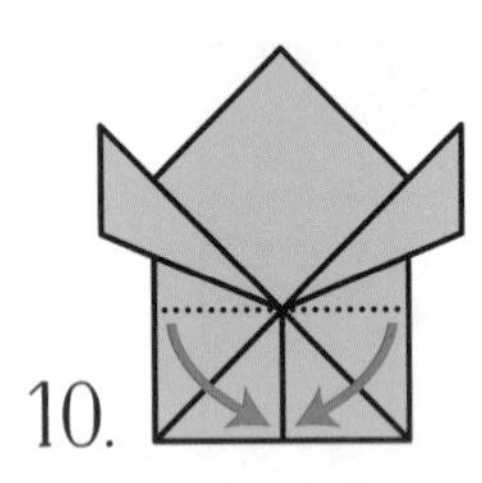

10.

Diagonally fold down the two top corners of the flap, created in step 9, to the centre of its lower edge and crease.

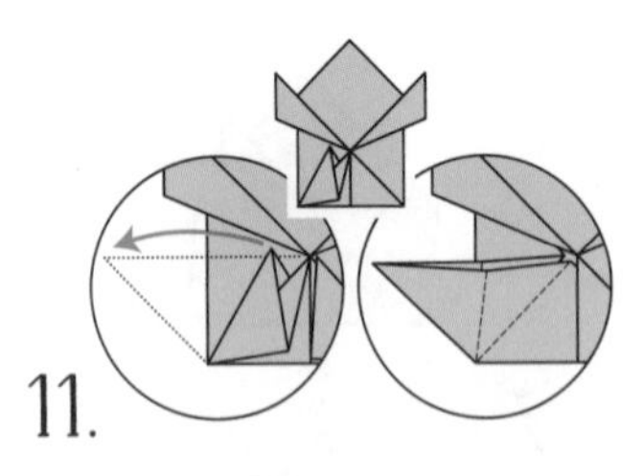

11.

Carefully prise out the top left point and open out the part as shown. Flatten and crease. Repeat with the right side.

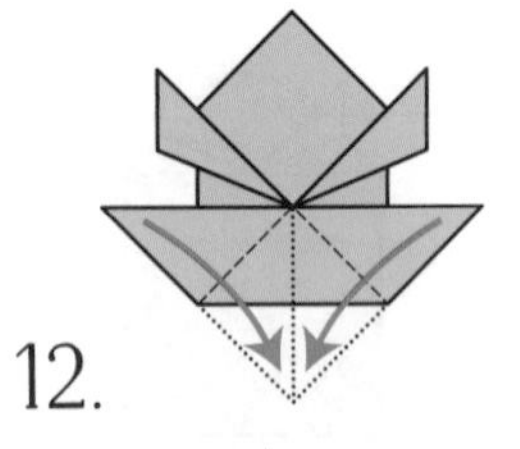

12.

Diagonally fold in the two new outer points to meet at a central point below the base of the model.

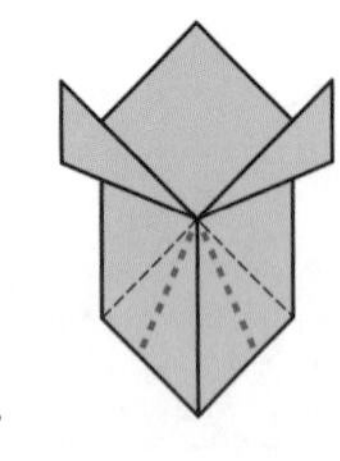

13.

The model frog should now look like this.

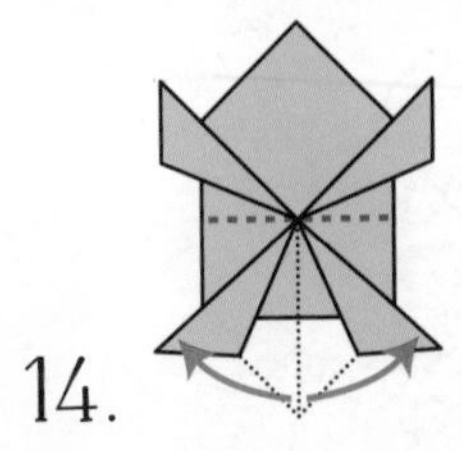

14.

Fold out the two centre points along the red dotted lines shown in step 13.

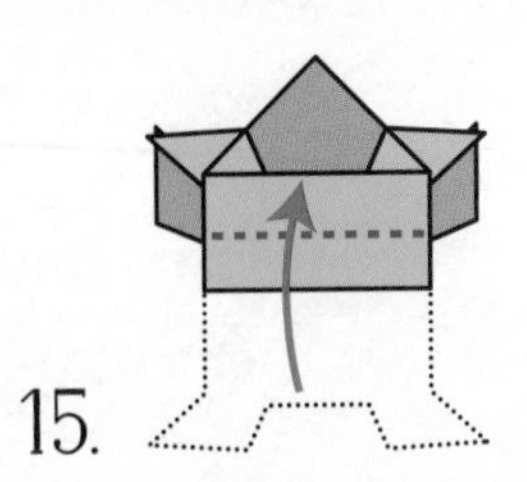

15.

Fold up the bottom half of the model along the line shown in step 14. By now the model will be getting quite thick so you will need to crease it well.

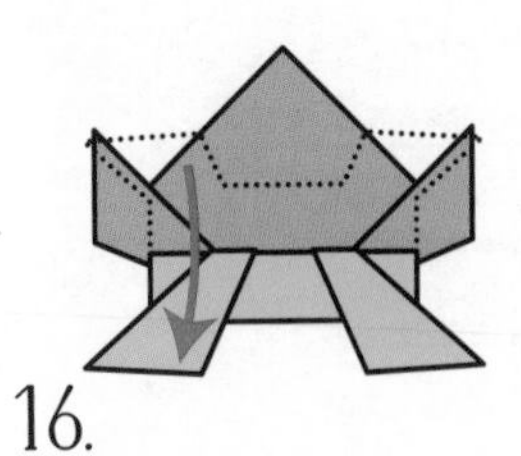

16.

Fold down half of the fold made in step 15 along the red dotted line shown in that diagram.

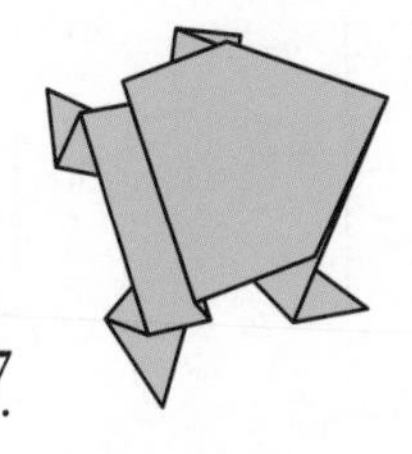

17.

Flip the model over and you have your frog model.

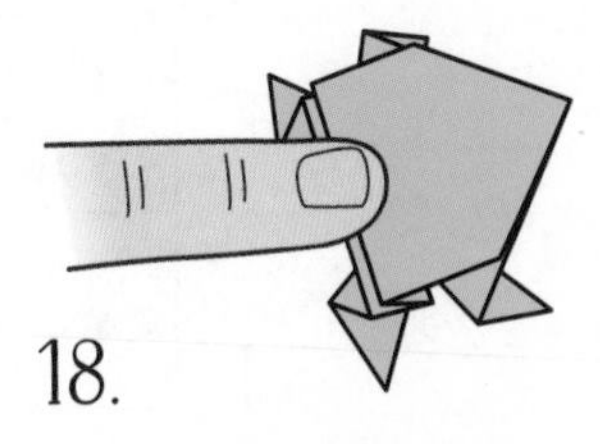

18.

Now make it jump by pulling back and pressing down the lower edge of its back, and letting the model spring out from under your finger.

PIG

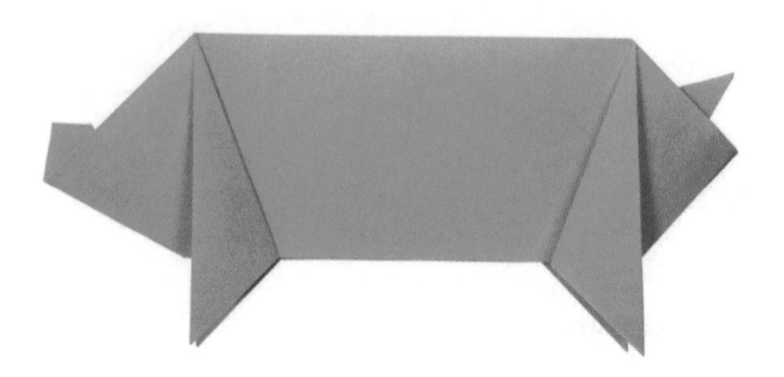

1\.

Place your square with the coloured side up. Fold the bottom edge up to the top. Crease and unfold.

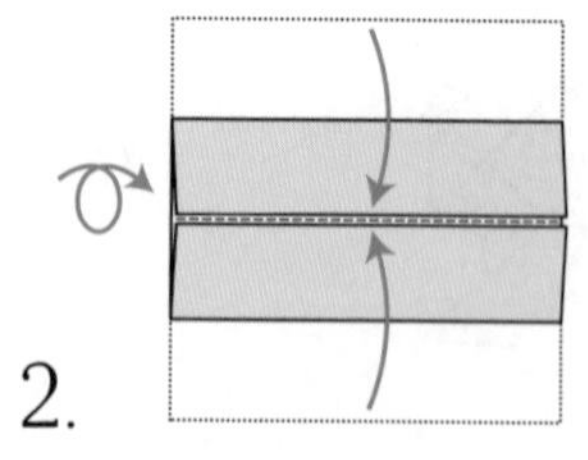

2\.

Turn the square over and fold the top edge down to the crease in the middle. Repeat with the bottom edge, folding it up to the crease in the middle.

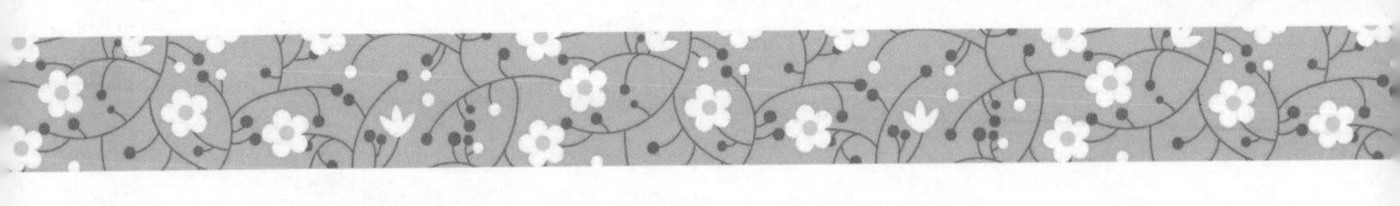

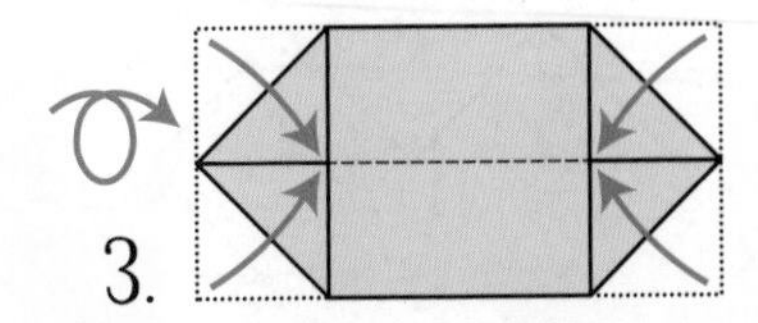

Turn the model over and fold the four corners in as shown.

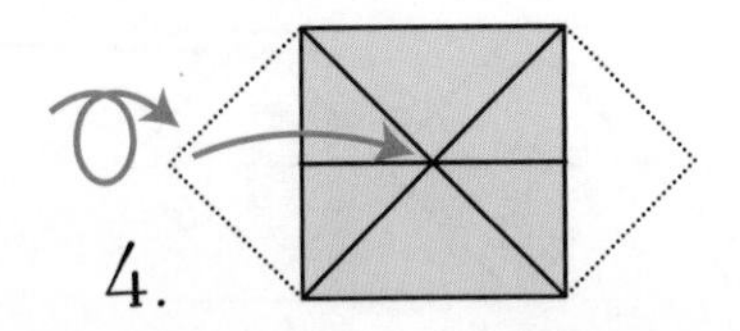

Turn the model over again and fold the left and right points into the centre and crease.

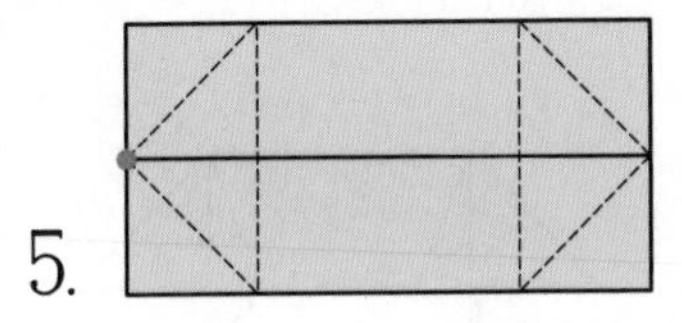

Undo the folds that you made in steps 3 and 4.

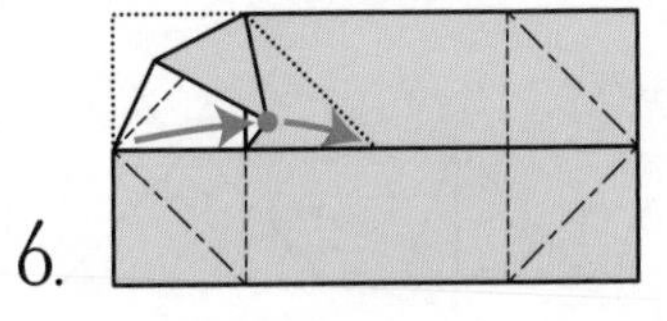

Take the left point on the top fold (shown in step 5) and fold it into the centre as shown. Crease flat.

7.

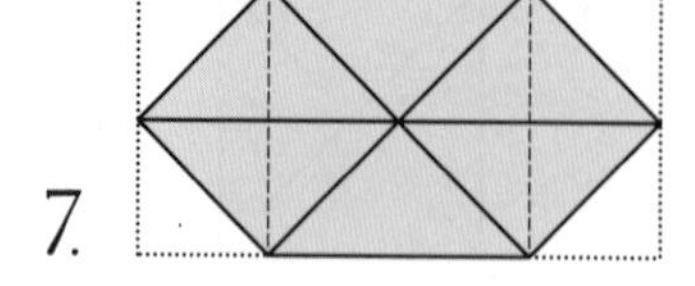

Repeat step 6 with the other 3 points.

8.

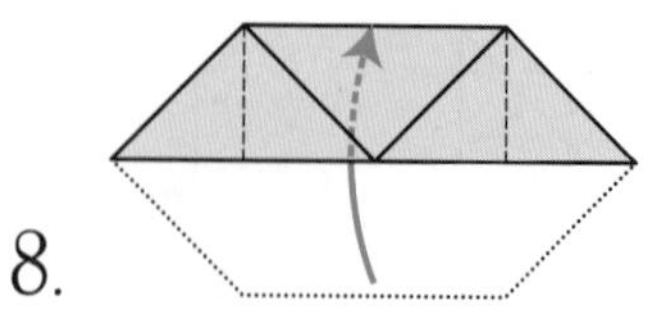

Fold the bottom half of the model up behind the top half and crease.

9.

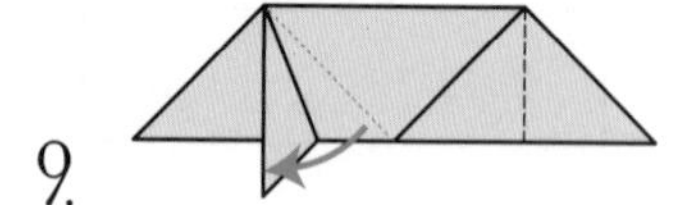

Fold down the left centre flap so that the long edge is vertical as shown and crease well.

10.

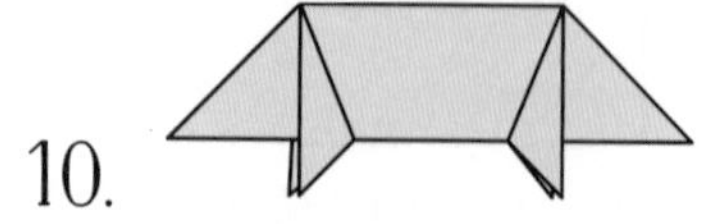

Repeat step 9 with the other three flaps to create the legs.

11.

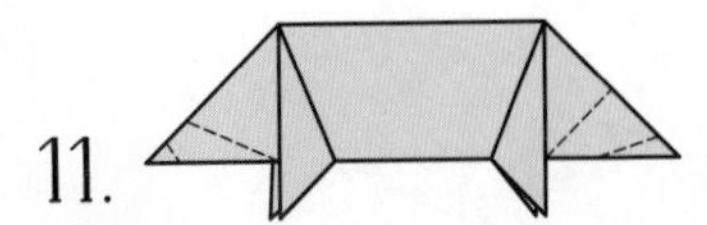

Crease and then unfold along the dashed lines indicated. Then crease the other way along the same lines and unfold.

12.

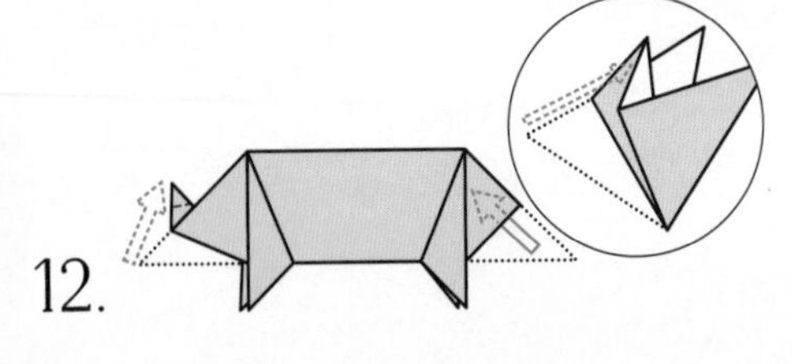

Make inside reverse folds along the longer lines (see the inset diagram).

13.

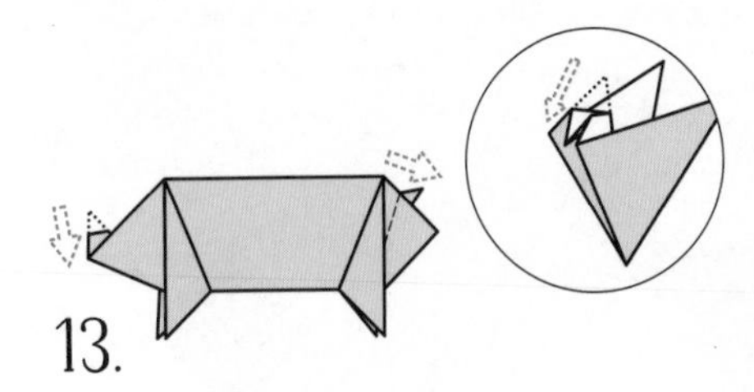

Now make inside reverse folds along the shorter lines to complete the model (see the inset diagram).

14.

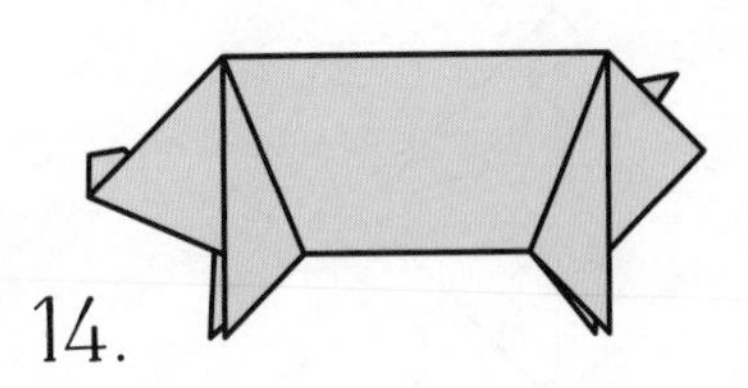

The finished model.

RABBIT

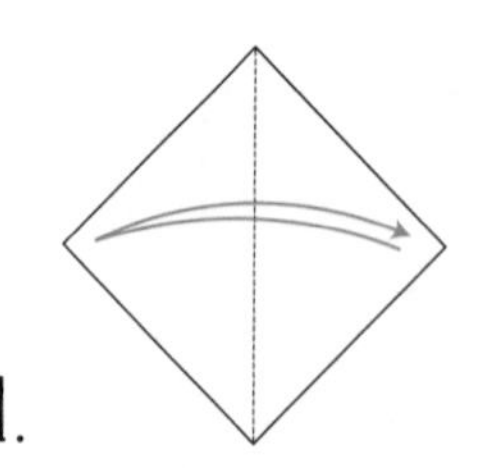

1.

Place your square diagonally with the white side up. Fold the right corner across to the left one. Crease and unfold.

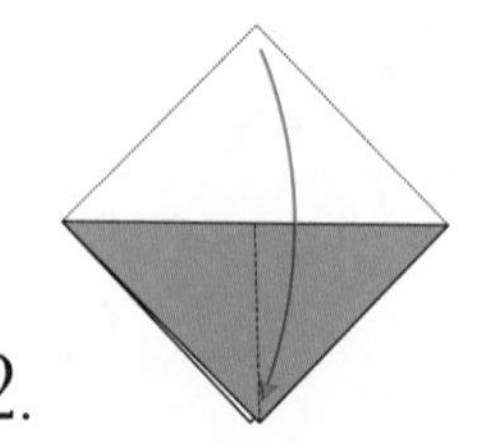

2.

Fold the top corner down to the bottom one, then crease.

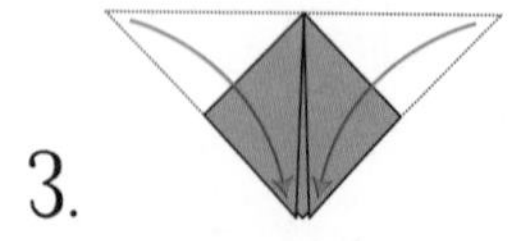

3.

Fold the left point down to the bottom centre corner and crease. Repeat with the right point.

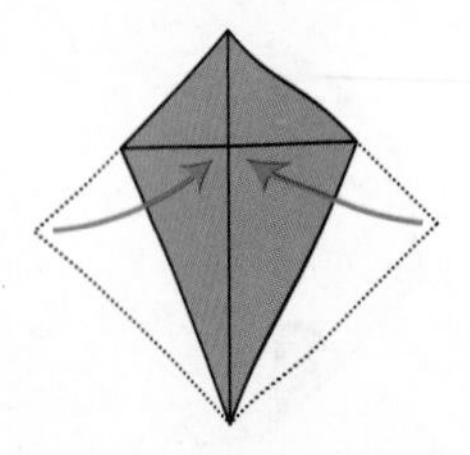

Fold the bottom left edge across to the centre line and crease, then repeat with the bottom right edge.

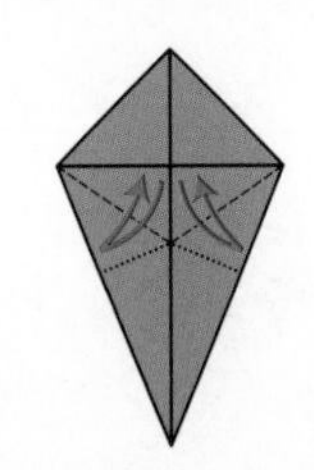

5.

Take the top of the left front flap and fold down diagonally until it lines up with the left bottom edge. Crease and unfold. Repeat with the right-hand side.

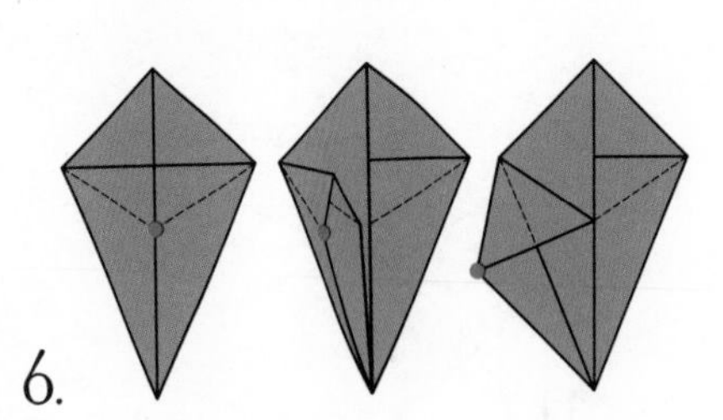

6.

Lift two layers of the left flap at the point where the new crease created in step 5 touches it. Spread out the flap as you pull across that point and flatten the new shape, as in the diagrams. Repeat with the right flap.

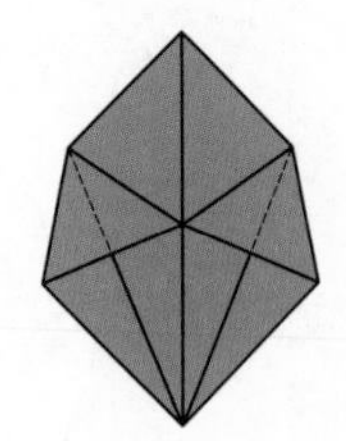

7.

Your model should now look like this.

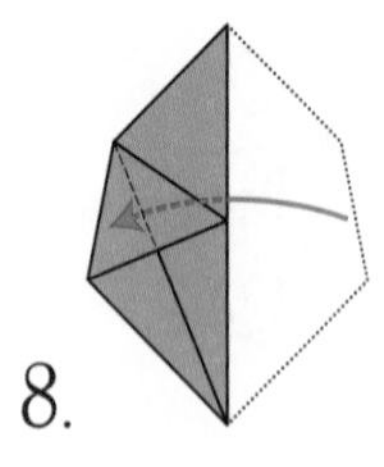

8.

Fold the right half of the model back behind the left half and crease.

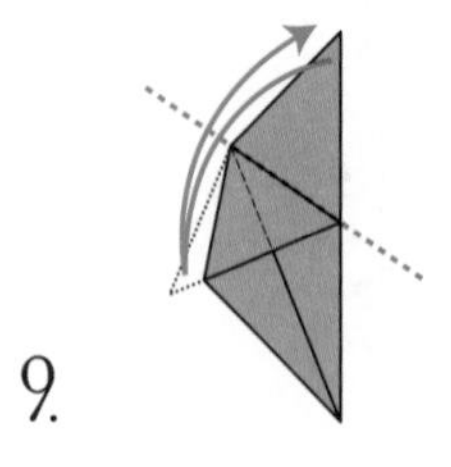

9.

Fold down the top part of the model along the red dotted line indicated in the diagram. Crease well, unfold and then fold the other way along the same line. Crease and unfold again.

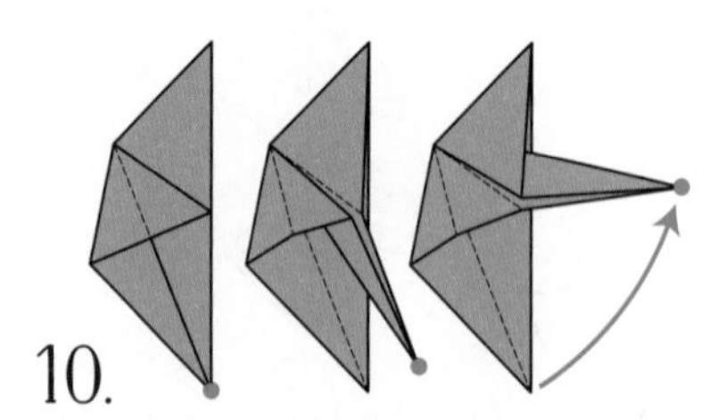

10.

Take the narrower front point and fold the creased edge underneath and upwards to the new position shown.

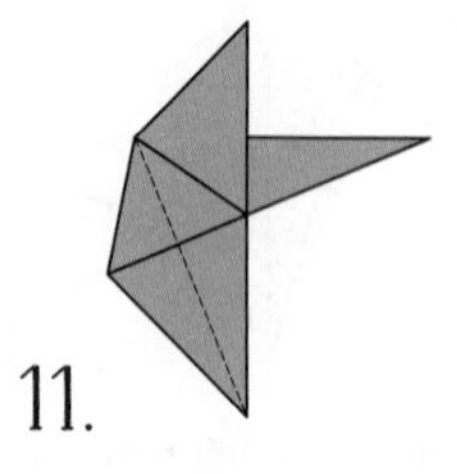

11.

Flatten and crease.

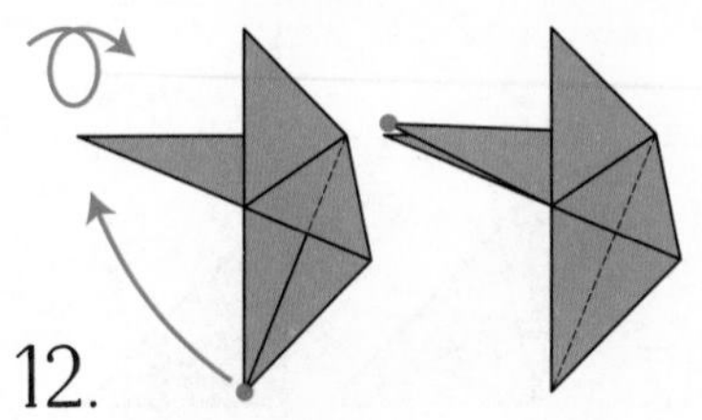

12.

Flip the model over and repeat steps 10 and 11 with the narrow bottom flap.

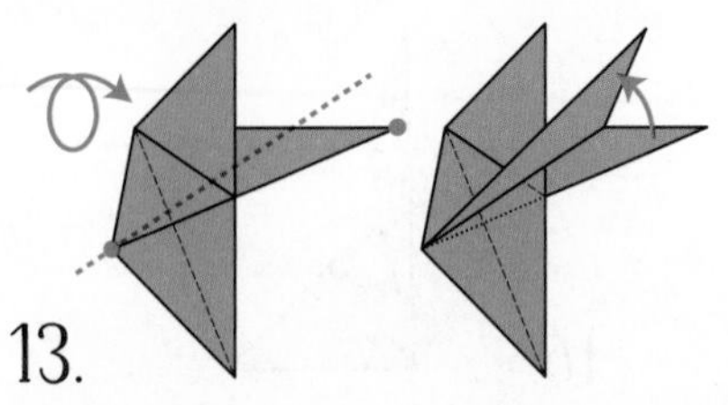

13.

Flip the model over. Take the long lower edge of the front flap, indicated between the two red points, and fold up along the dotted red line in the diagram. Crease well.

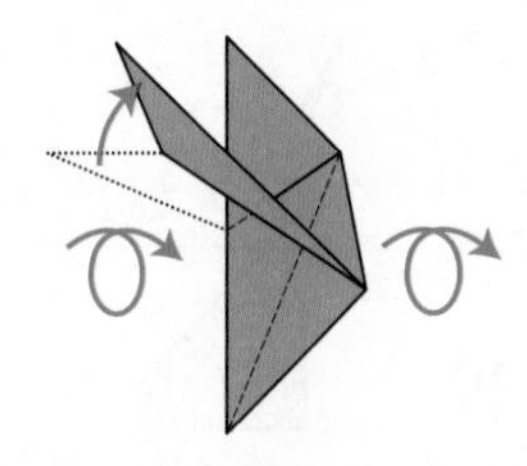

14.

Flip the model over and repeat step 13 with the other side. Flip the model over again.

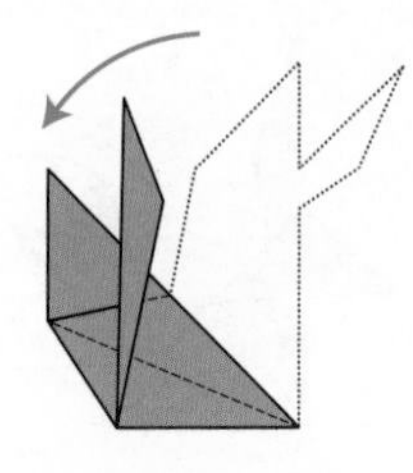

15.

Turn the model 45° anti-clockwise. This is the way the model will stand when finished.

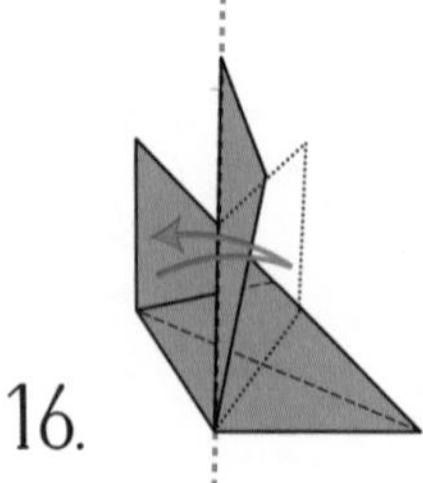

16.

Fold across the left part of the model along the red dotted line indicated in the diagram. Crease well, unfold and then fold the other way along the same line. Crease and unfold again.

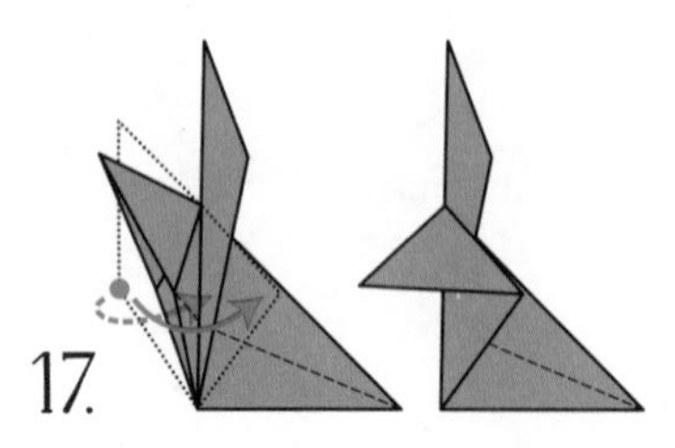

17.

Open the two sides at the front of the model. Fold both back on each side and crease and flatten well.

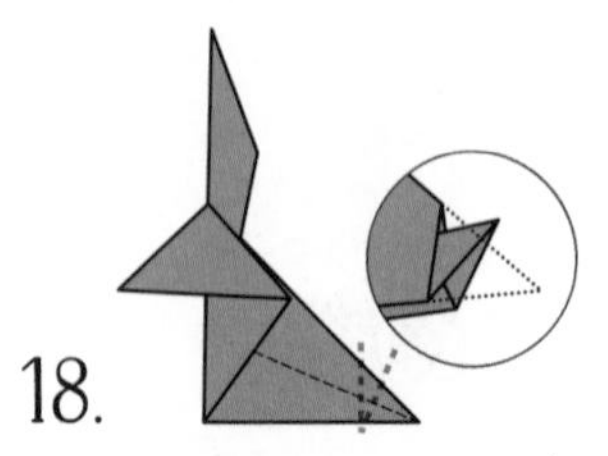

18.

Fold, crease and unfold the tail along the lines indicated. Repeat the other way. Inside reverse fold along the longer fold and then inside reverse fold along the shorter one.

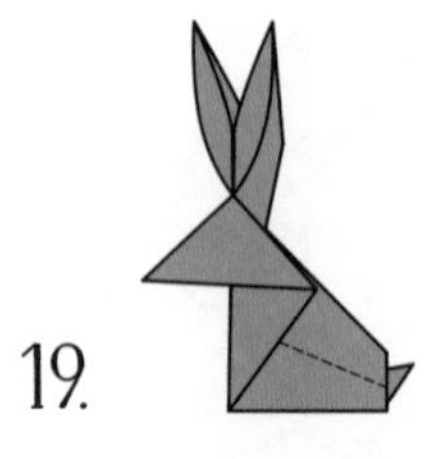

19.

Open out and shape each ear. You will now have completed a very difficult model. Well done!

ROSE

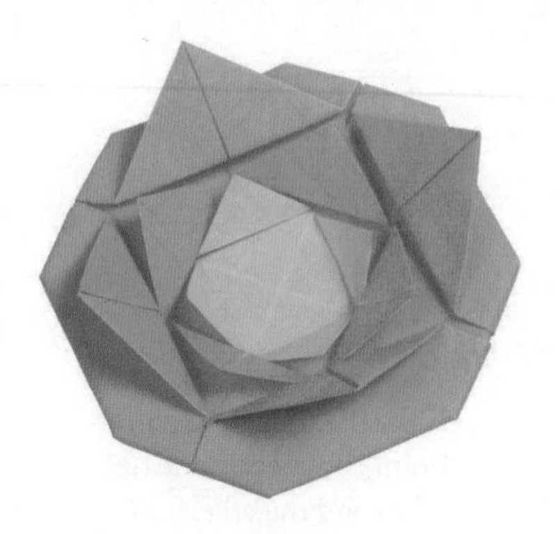

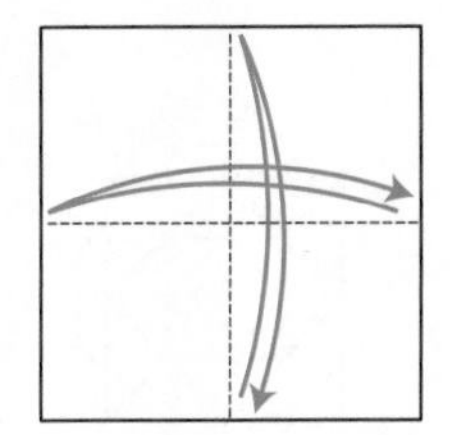

1.

With the white side up, fold the bottom edge to the top, crease and unfold. Fold the right edge to the left, crease and unfold.

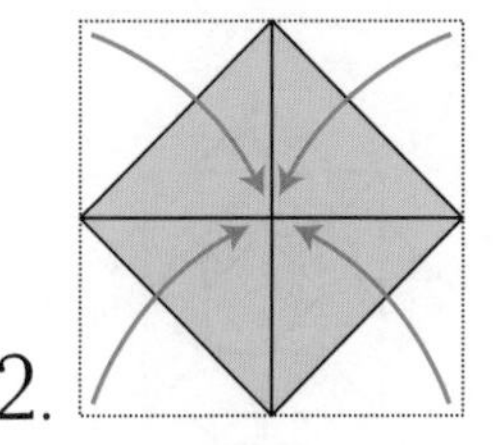

2.

Fold the four corners into the centre and crease the four sides.

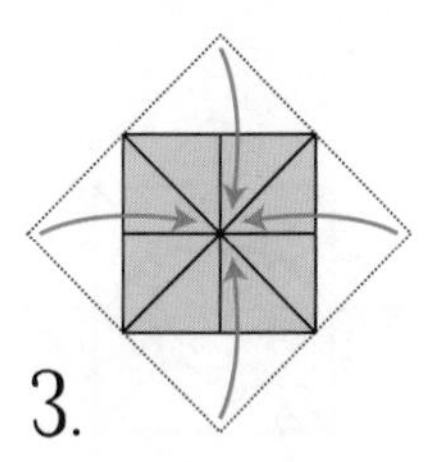

3.

Fold the four new corners into the centre and crease the four sides.

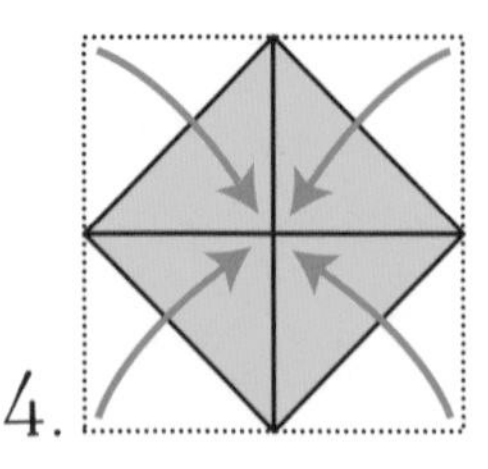

Repeat step 3 with the four new corners.

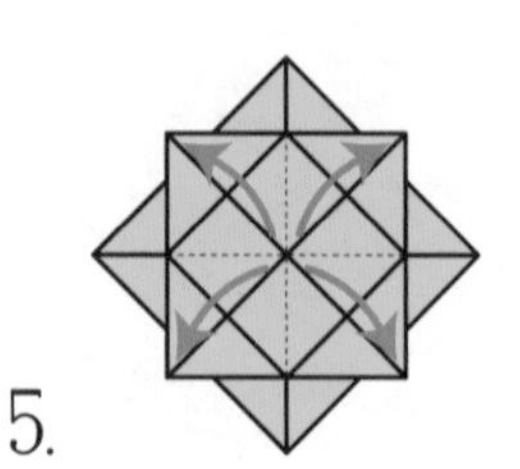

Take the four top centre points, fold each one out beyond the edge and crease, as per the diagram.

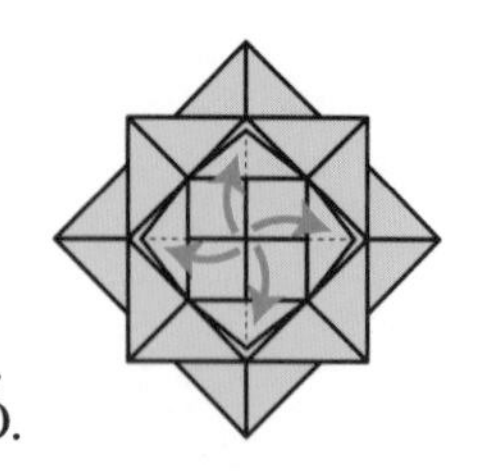

Take the next four centre points and fold them out and crease as shown.

Take the last four centre points and fold and crease them as shown.

Fold back and crease the four outer corners of the base. Crease well.

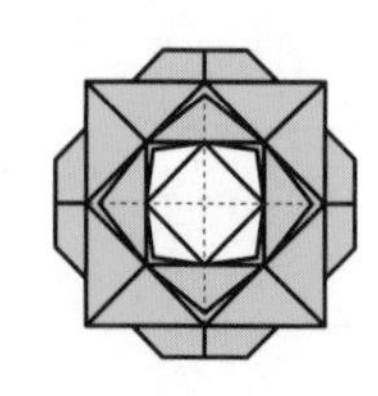

Carefully lift and position the twelve petals as per the diagram.

STAR BOX

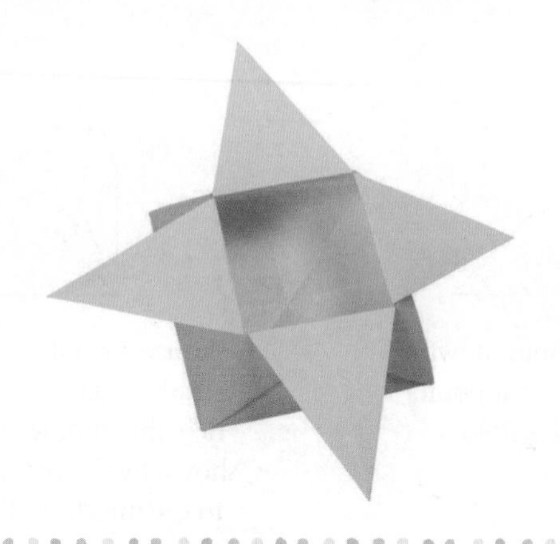

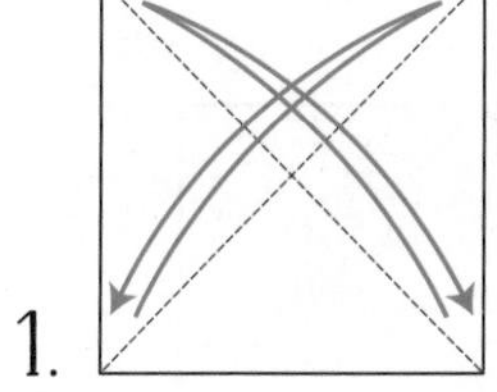

1.

With the white side up, fold the bottom left corner to the top right. Crease and unfold. Fold the bottom right corner to the top left and unfold.

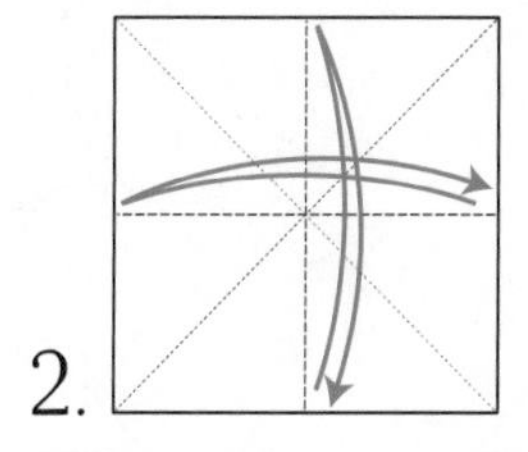

2.

Fold the bottom edge up to the top one. Crease and unfold. Then repeat by folding the right edge over to the left one. Crease and unfold.

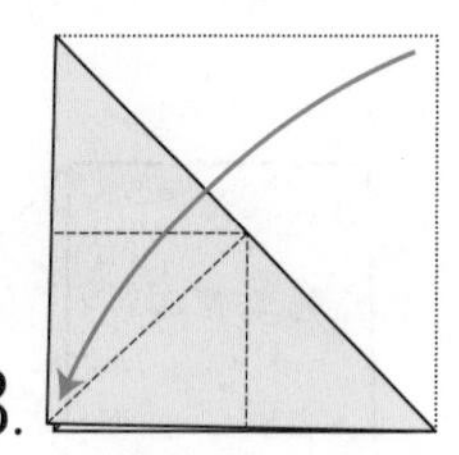

3.

Fold the top right corner down to the bottom left one.

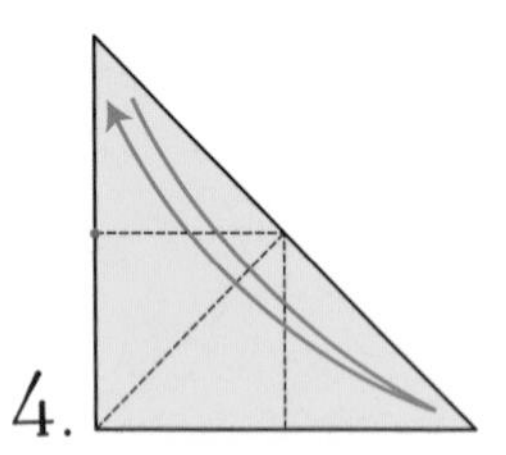

4.

Fold the top point down
to the bottom right point.
Crease and unfold.

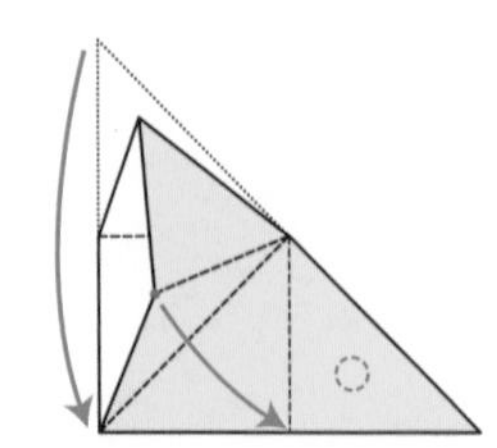

5.

With your right hand hold the model
steady where the red circle is shown.
Take the middle of the front left edge,
shown by the red dot, and pull it down
to the middle of the base and crease.

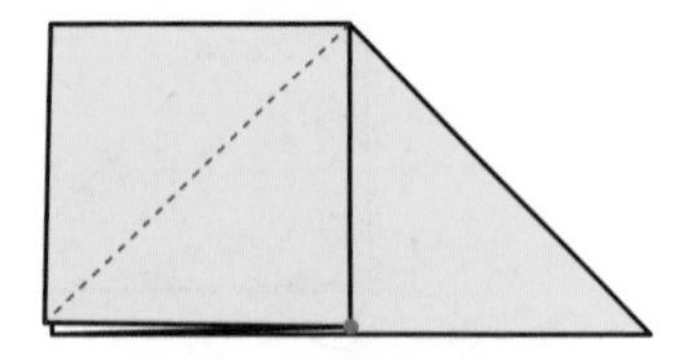

6. This is how your model
should look now.

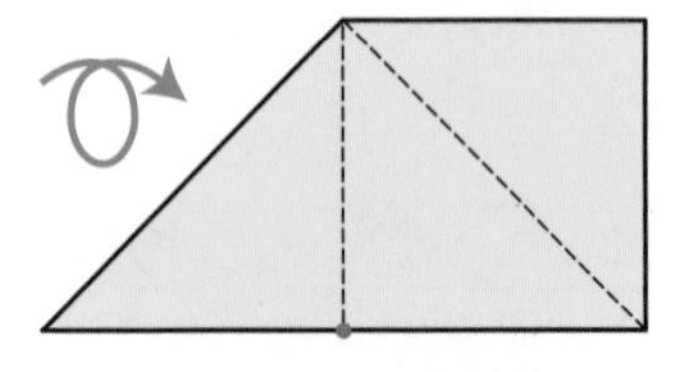

7. Flip the model over.

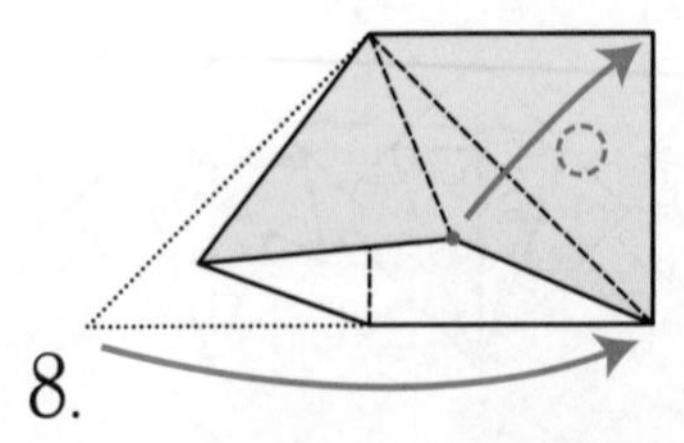

8.

Holding the model steady with your right hand where the red circle is shown, lift up the middle of the front bottom edge, shown by the red dot and take it to the top right corner.

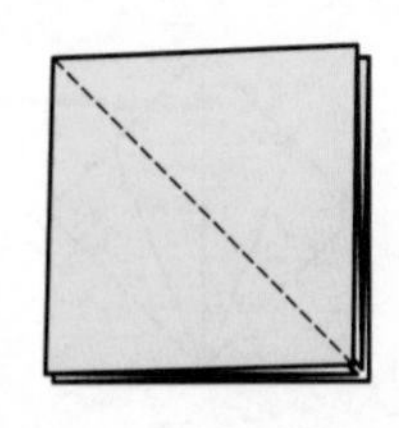

9.

Your model should now look like this.

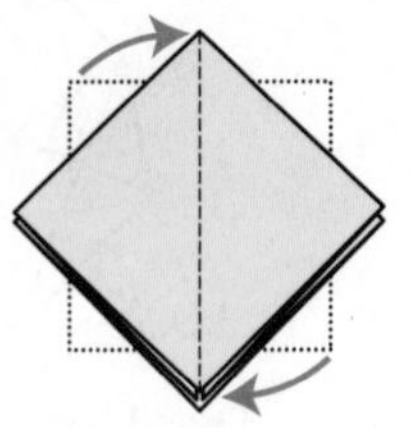

10.

Turn the model 45° clockwise so that the corner with four points is at the bottom.

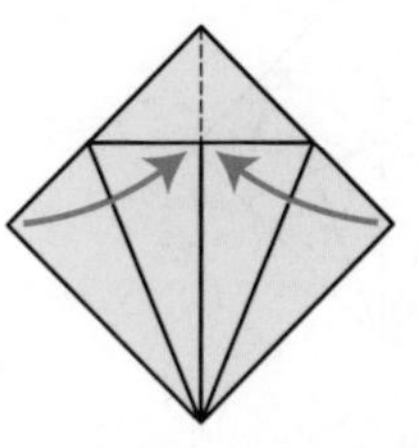

11.

Fold the front bottom left edge across to the centre line and crease, then repeat with the front bottom right edge.

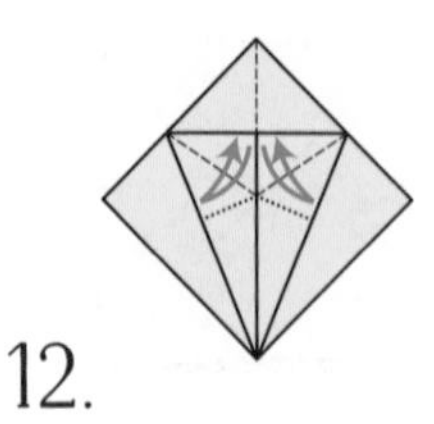

12.

Take the top central corner of the left front flap and fold down diagonally until it lines up with the left bottom edge. Crease and unfold. Repeat with the right-hand side.

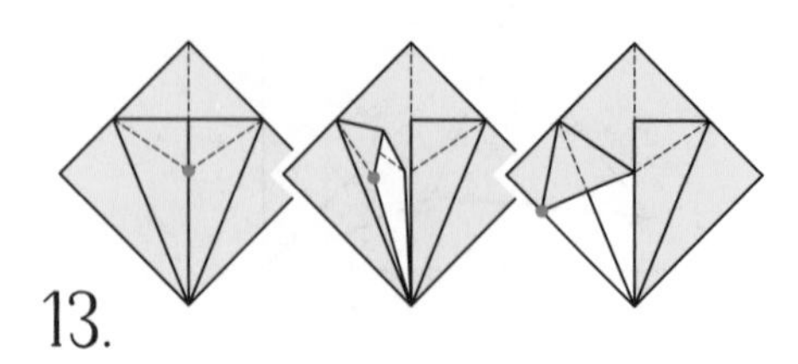

13.

Lift the edge of the left flap at the point shown by the red dot. Spread out the flap as you pull that point across and flatten the new shape, as shown in the diagrams. Repeat with the right flap.

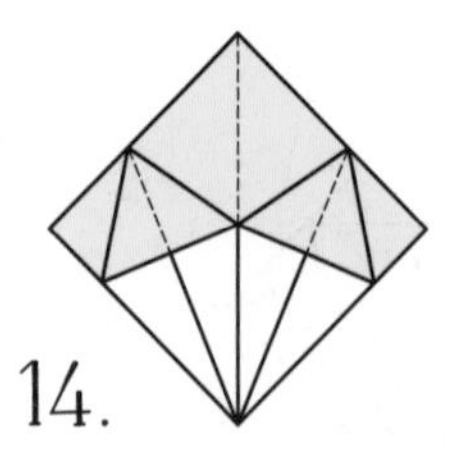

14.

Your model should now look like this.

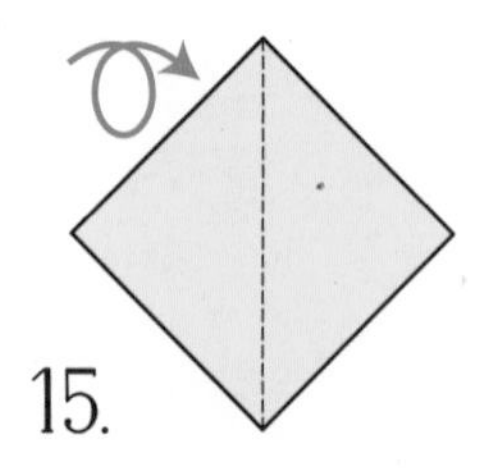

15.

Flip the model over and repeat steps 11, 12 and 13.

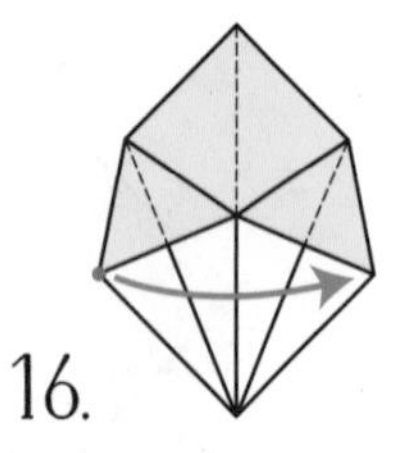

16.

Take the front left half of the model at the point shown, fold it over to the right and crease.

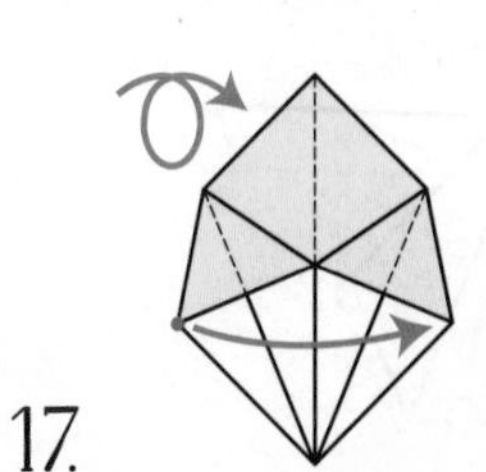

17.

Flip the model over and repeat step 16 by folding the top left flap over to the right and crease.

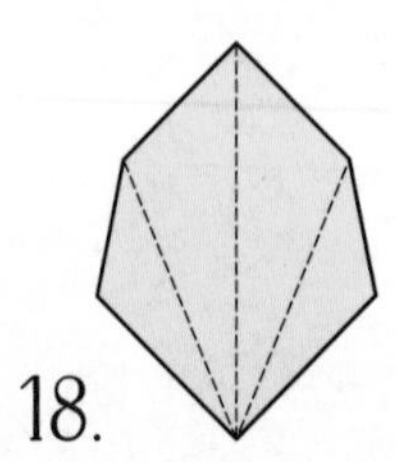

18.

Your model should now look like this.

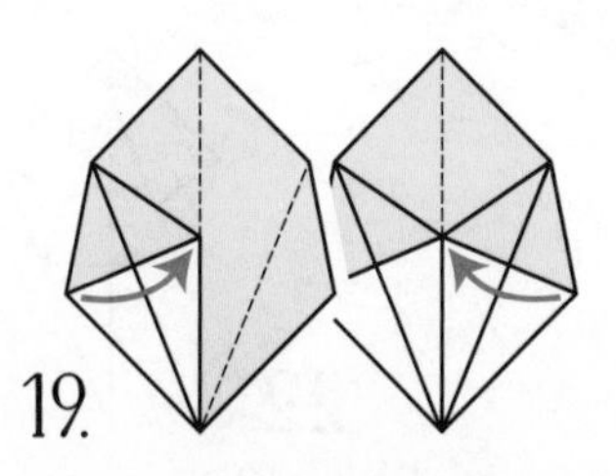

19.

Fold the front left triangular flap into the centre as shown, then repeat with the front right flap.

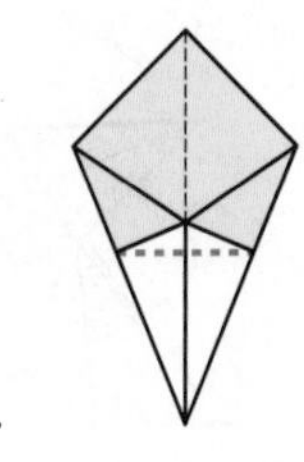

20.

Flip the model over and repeat step 19 with this side so that the model looks like this.

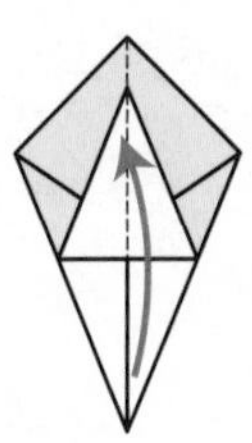

21.

Fold up the front bottom point along the red line indicated in the diagram for step 20 and crease. Flip the model over and repeat with the other side.

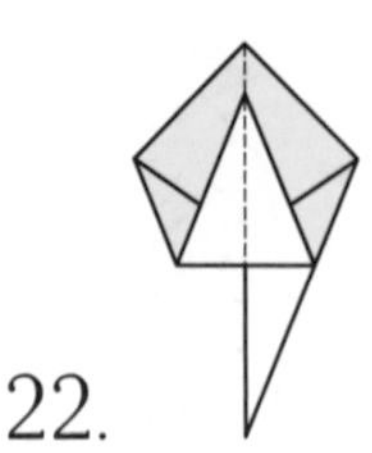

22.

Fold the front left half of the model over to the right and crease. Then fold up the front bottom point as in step 21 so that the model now looks like this.

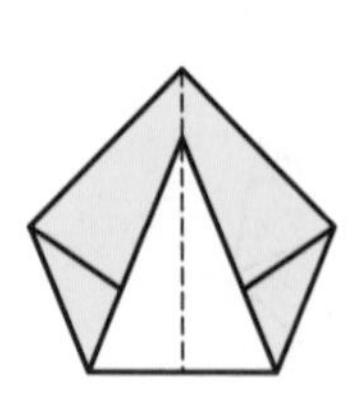

23.

Flip the model over and fold the front left half of the model over to the right and crease. Fold up the bottom point as in step 21 and crease. Your model should now look like this.

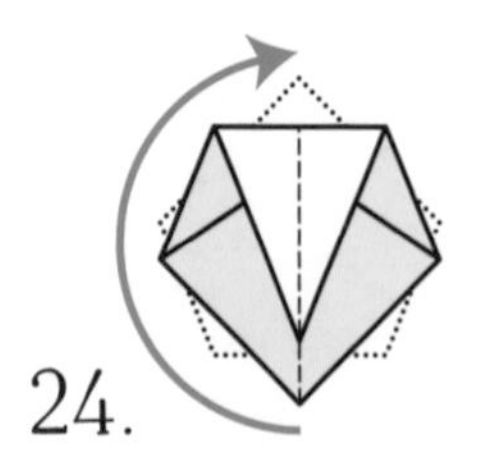

24.

Turn the model 180° clockwise.

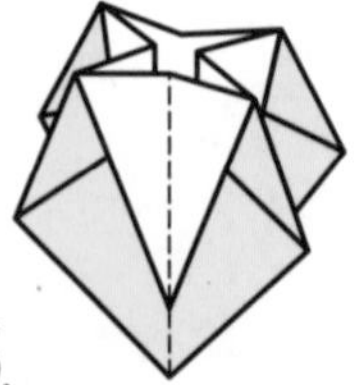

25.

Carefully open out the four sides and, by using your fingers inside the box, push out the sides and flatten the bottom.

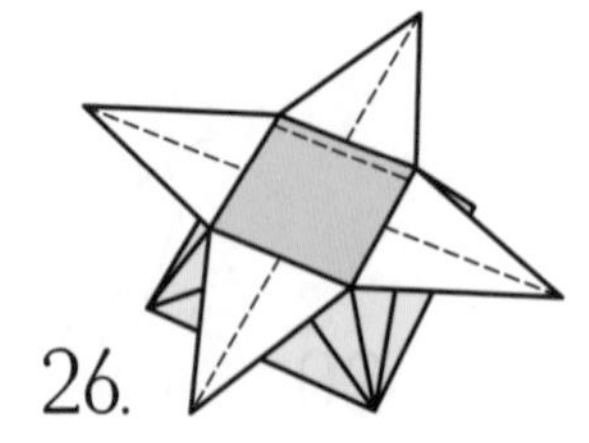

26.

Carefully crease the bottom four edges to create the base of the finished box.

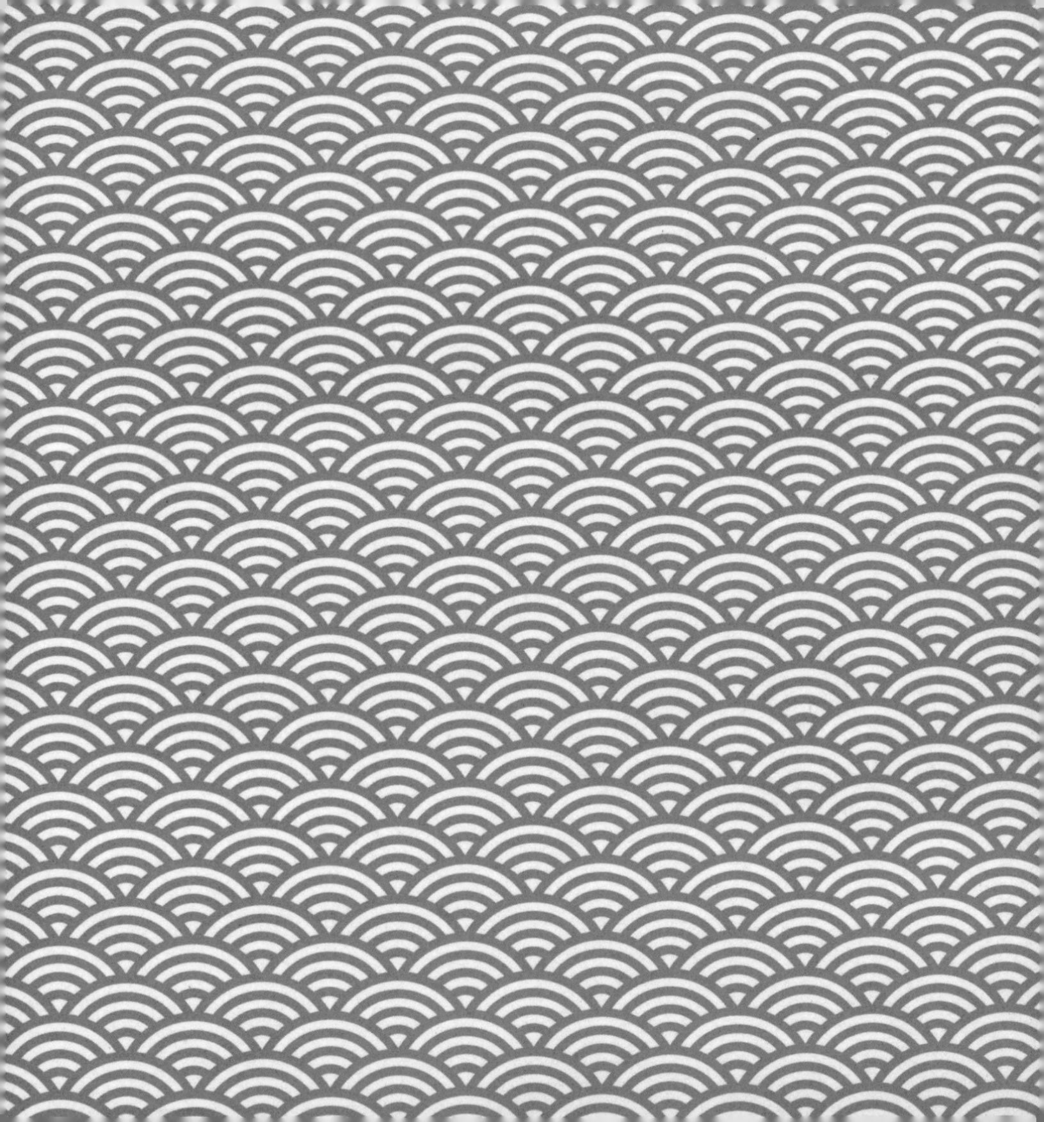

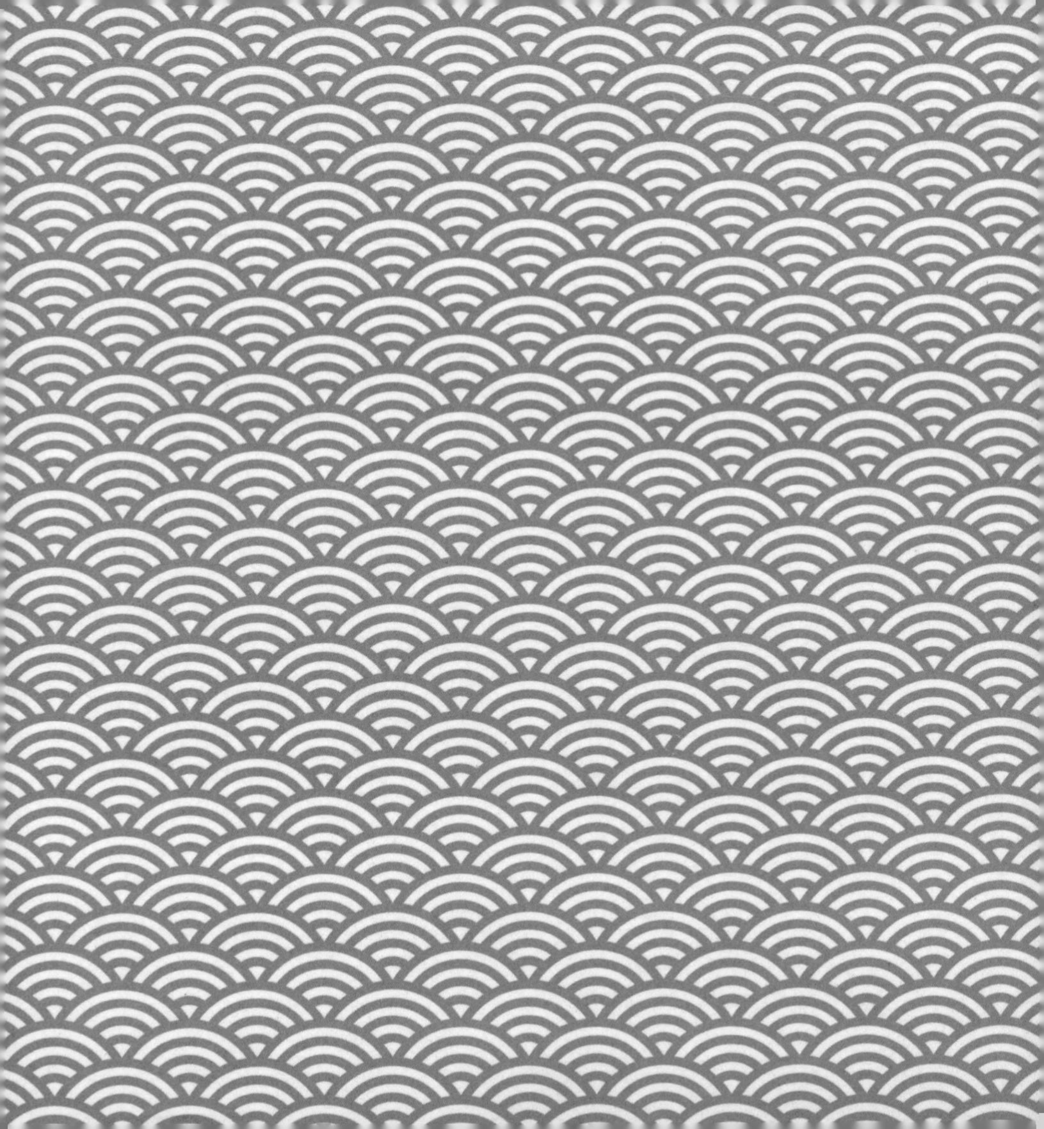

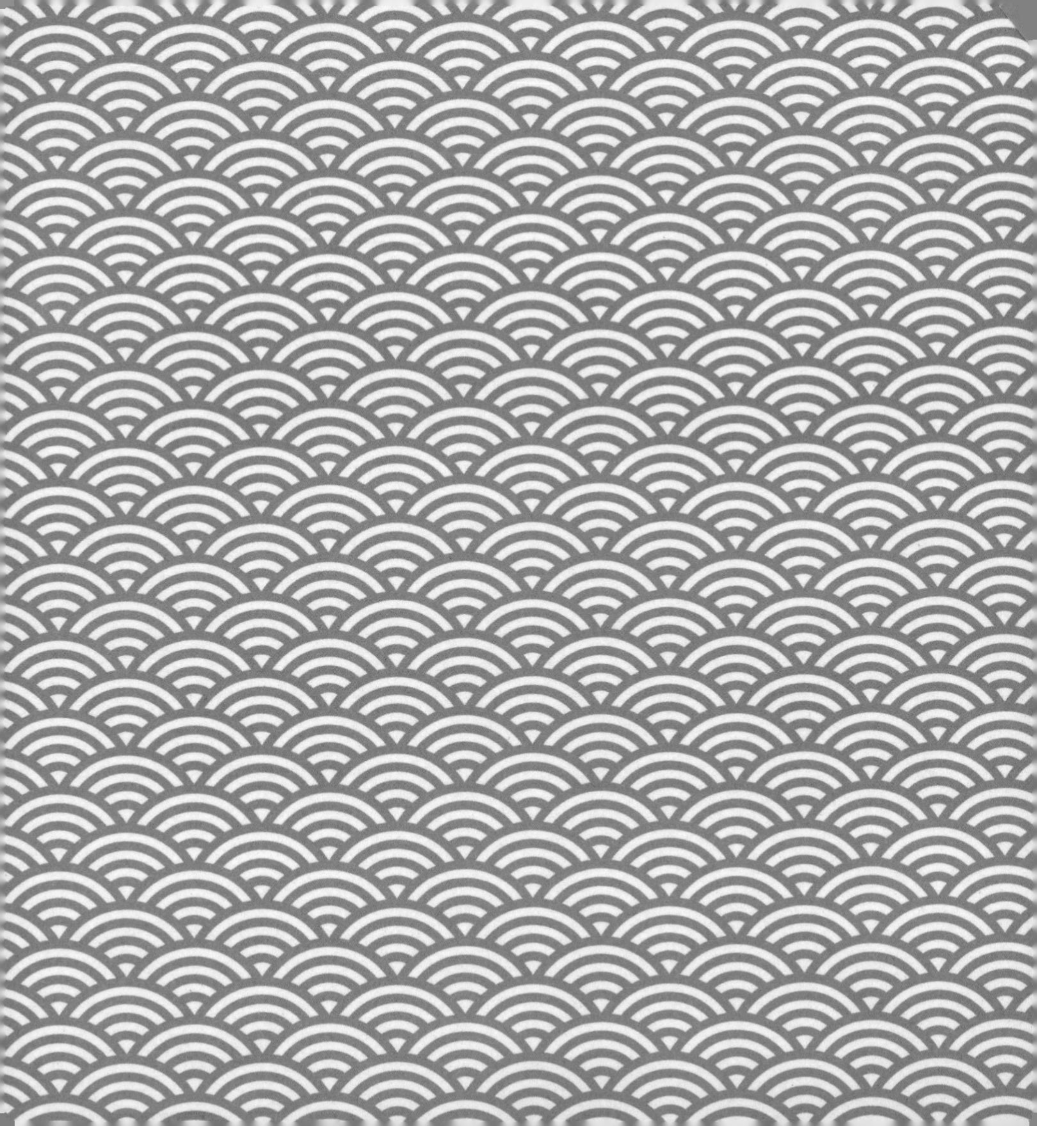

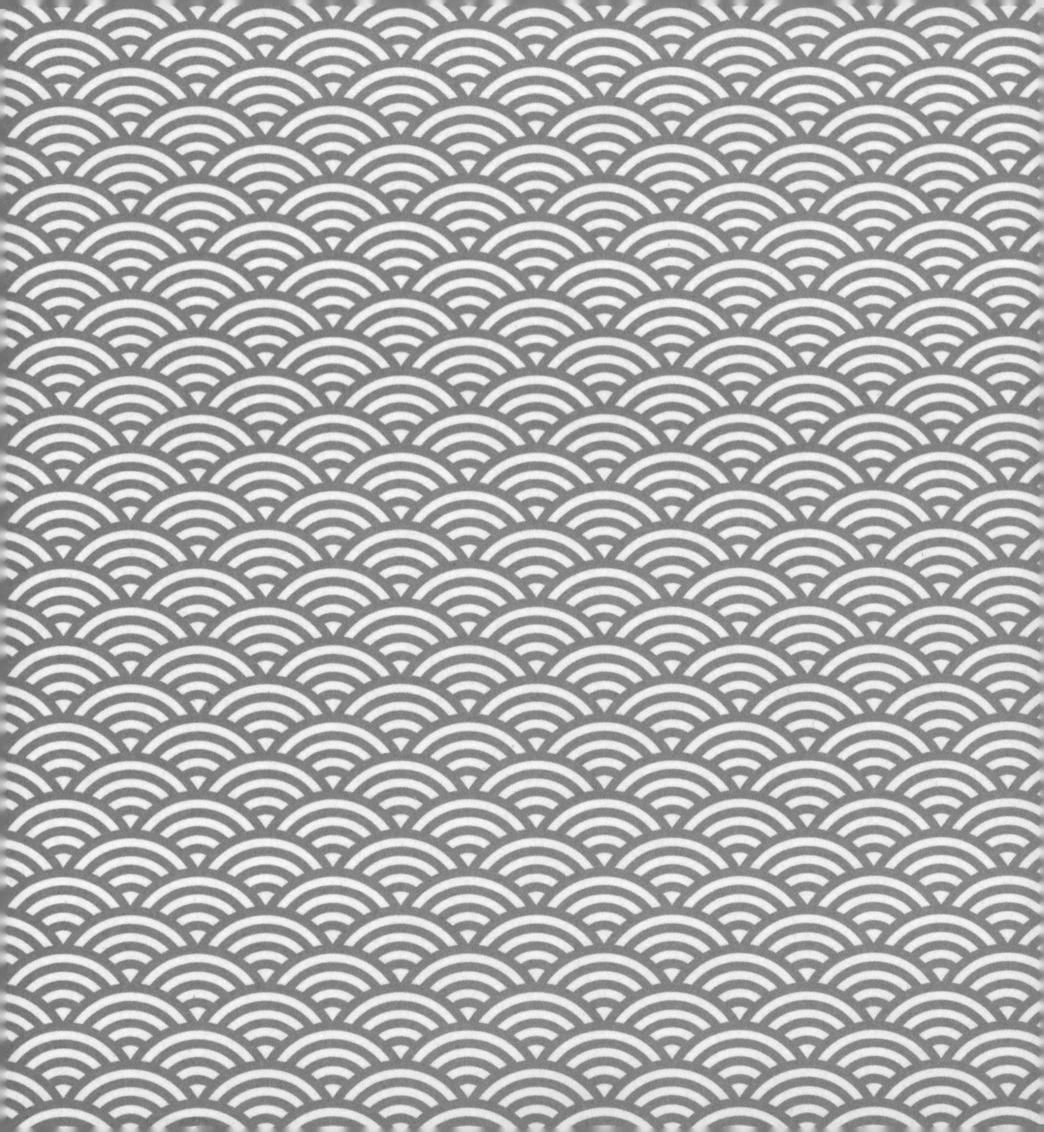

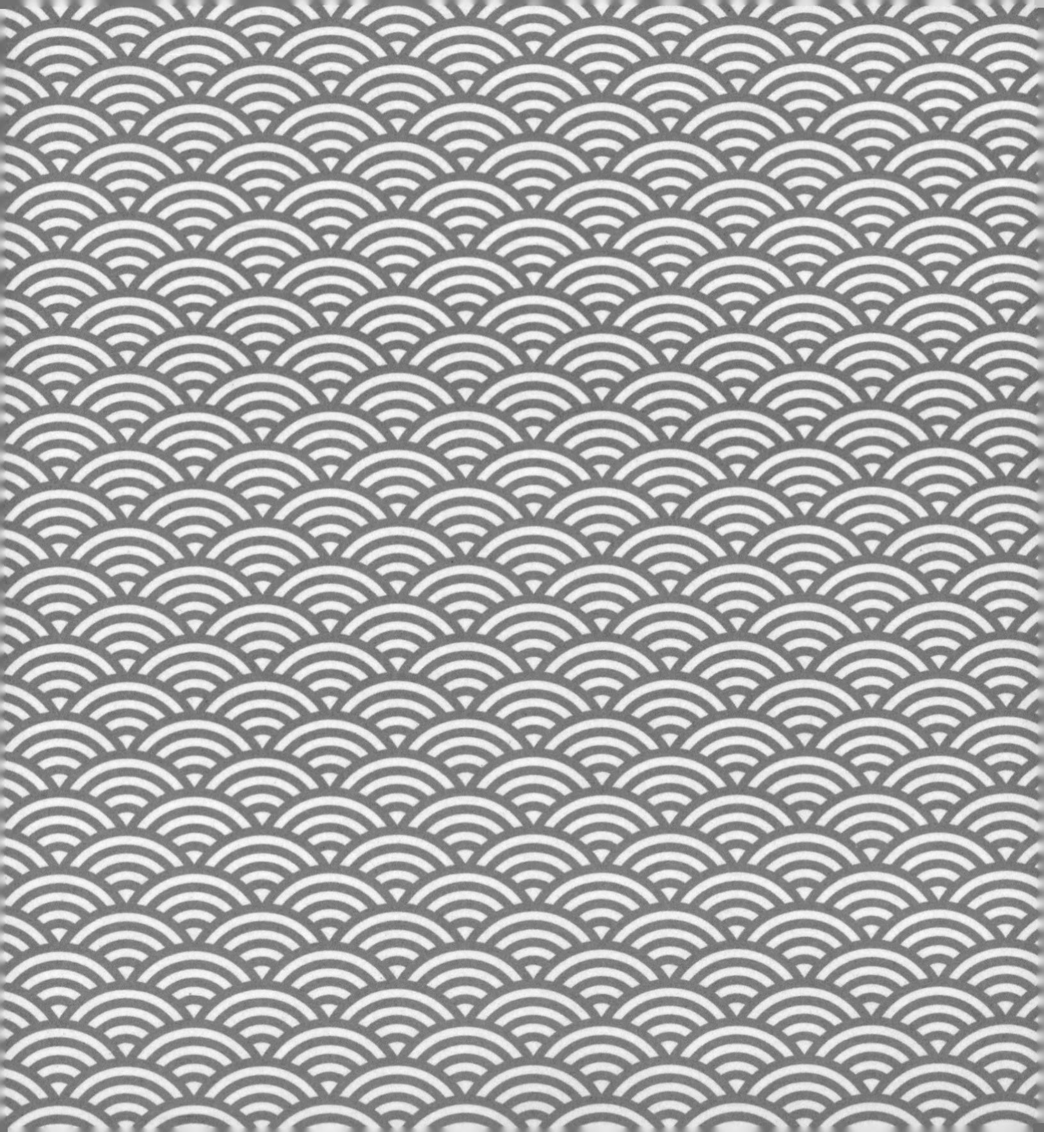

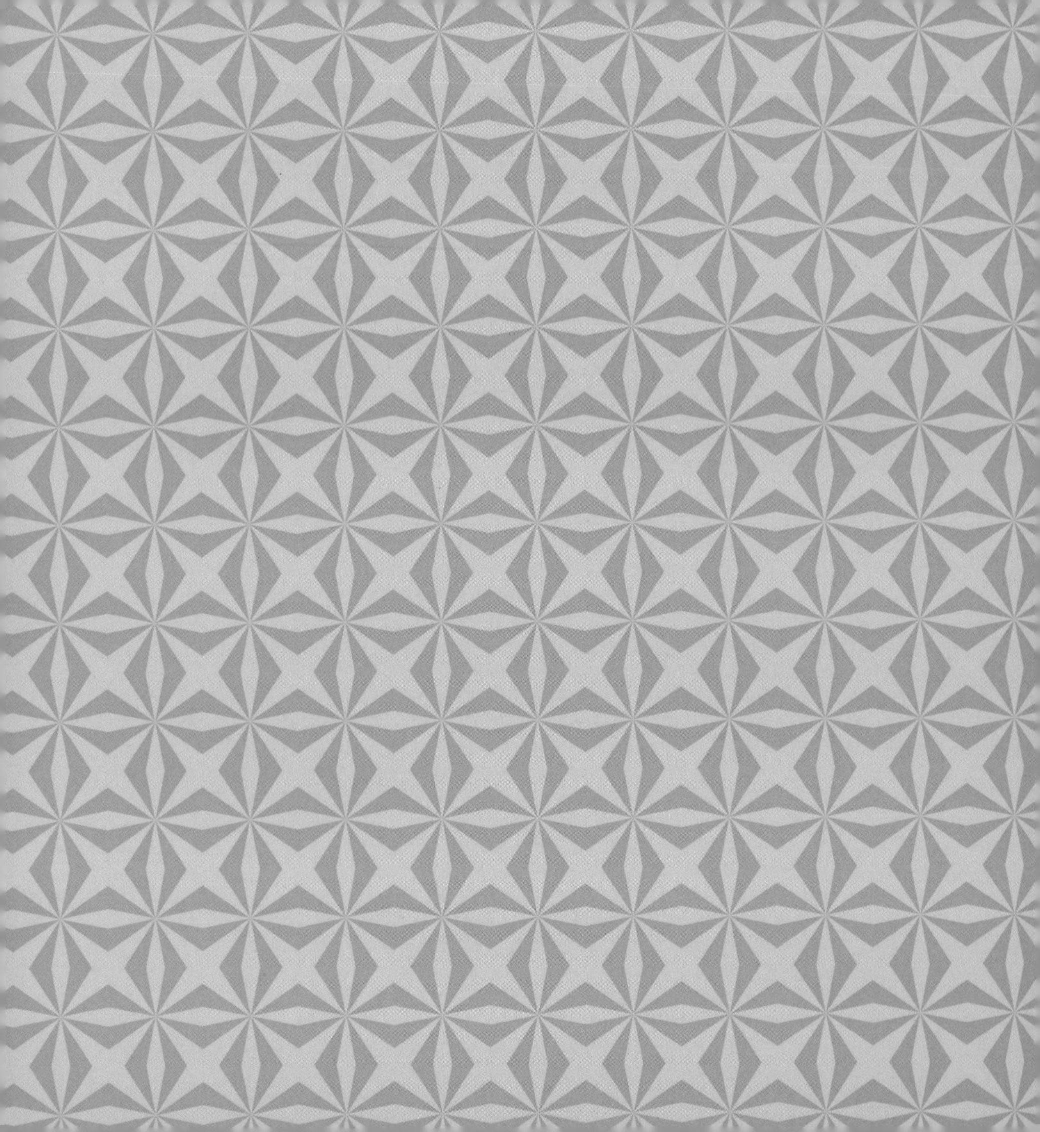

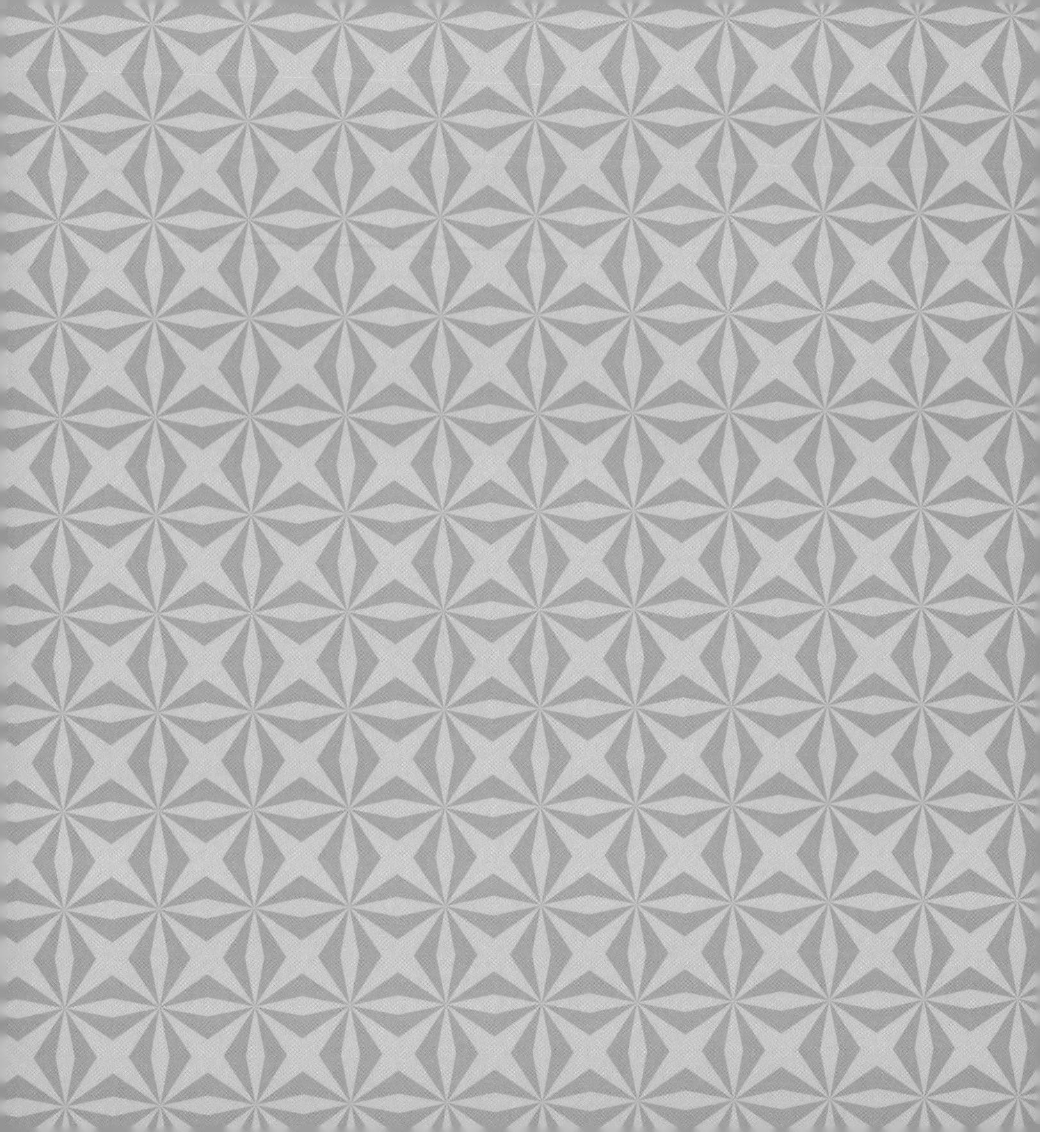

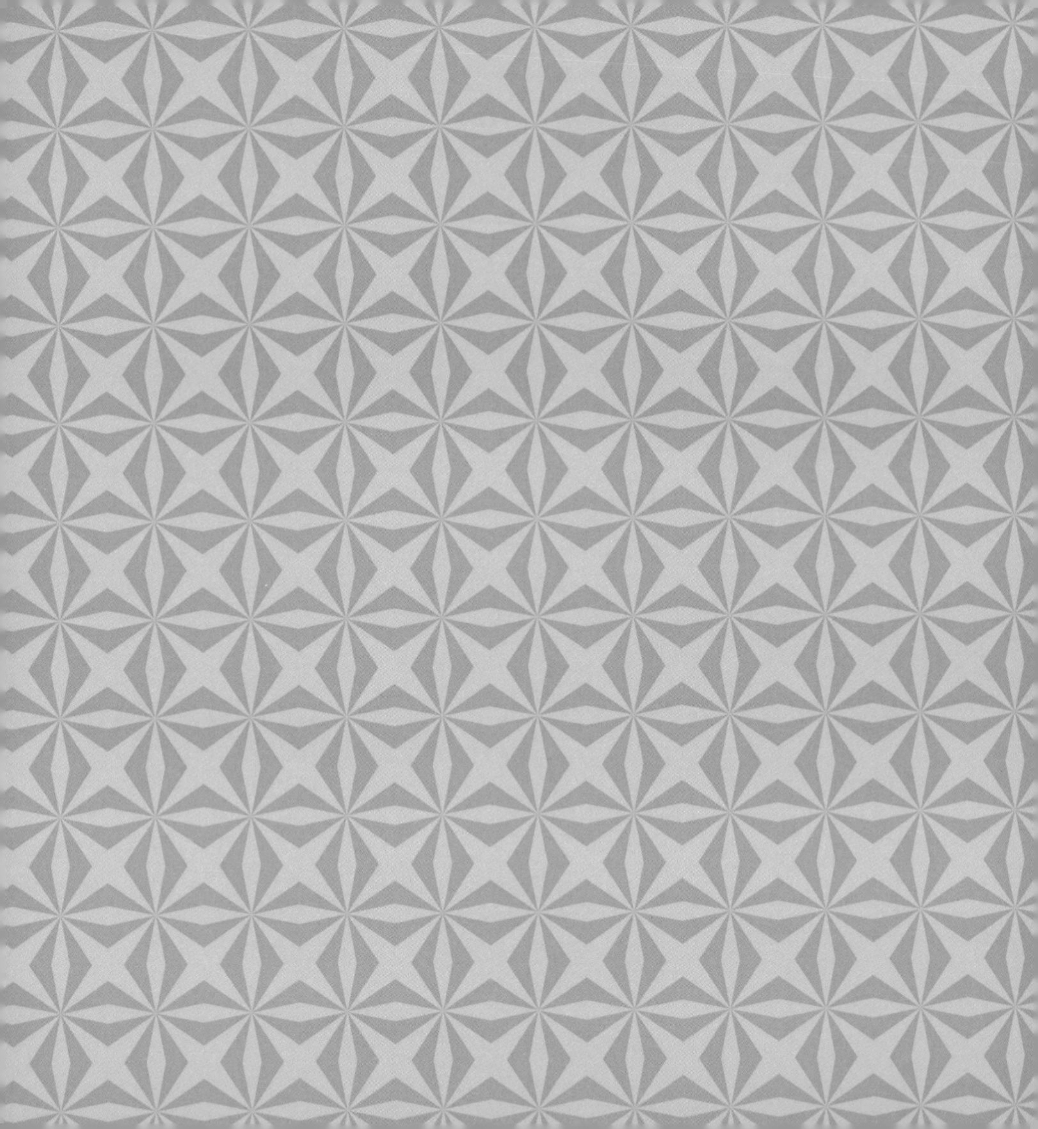

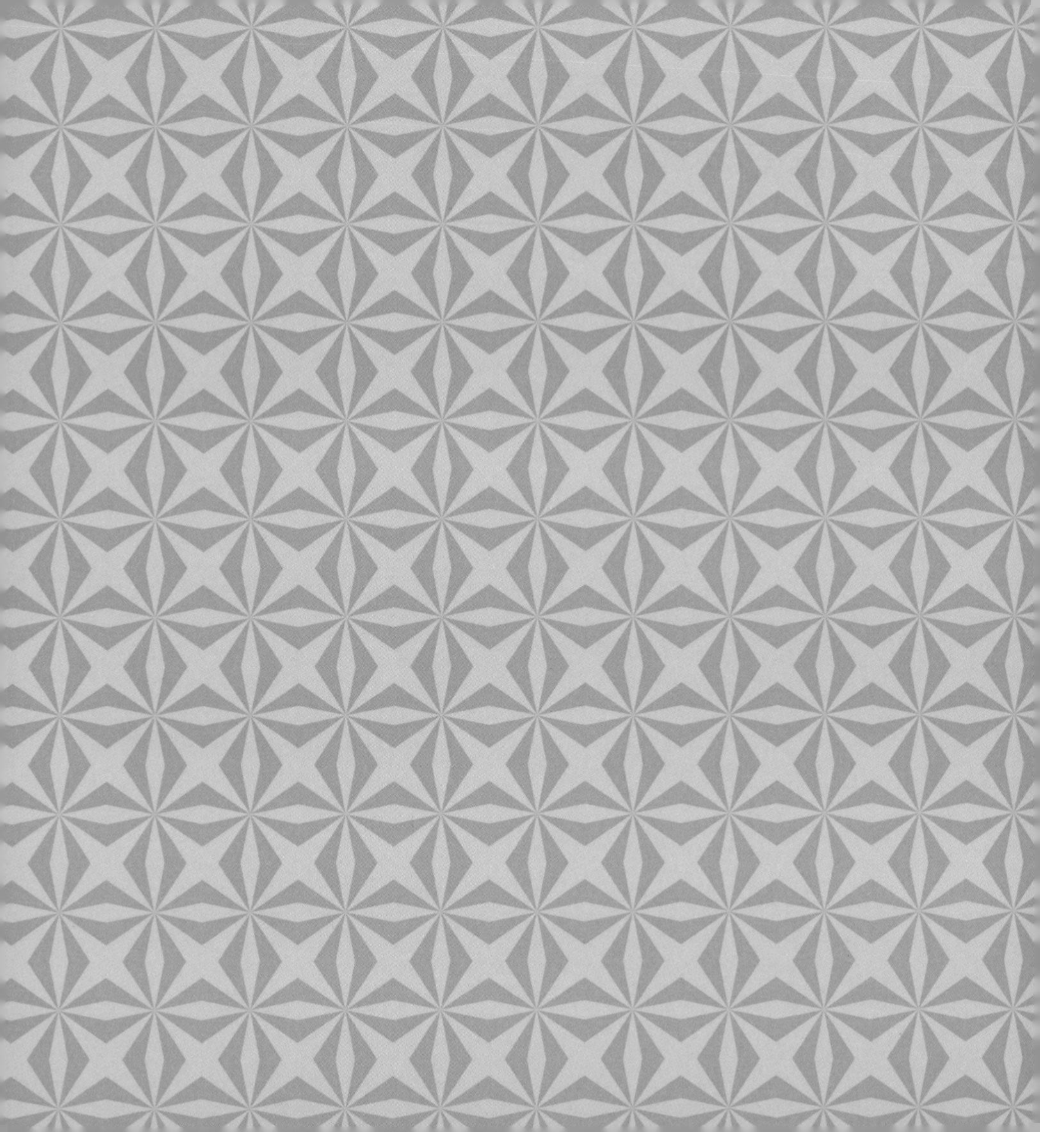